Applied Mechanics
FLUIDS

This book is a part of the

ALLYN AND BACON SERIES IN MECHANICAL
ENGINEERING AND APPLIED MECHANICS

Consulting Editor, FRANK KREITH
University of Colorado

Applied Mechanics: FLUIDS

Aldor C. Peterson
Iowa State University

ALLYN AND BACON, INC.   BOSTON

Contents

Preface

The text presents the basics of fluid mechanics without considering the more complex problems that may occur in hydraulic situations. The emphasis is on basic principles and their application in practical fluid mechanics problems. Examples, which are included after each new concept, will assist the student in his understanding of the subject matter. The Bernoulli equation has been used as a basis for the derivation of all equations of fluid flow.

The subject matter in this text may be understood with or without a knowledge of calculus. A continuity of treatment is provided in either case. The material in Chapter 11 requires an understanding of impulse and momentum in the field of dynamics. In some courses in fluids this chapter may be omitted. If it is not omitted, sufficient explanation of the impulse and momentum concept may be given to permit its inclusion.

Chapter 12 is an introduction into the field of experimental analysis and model study as it may be applied to more complex fluid problems.

The author is indebted to the Crane Company and to Dr. Glenn Murphy for many of the tables and graphs appearing in this text.

ALDOR C. PETERSON
Ames, Iowa

Applied Mechanics
FLUIDS

SYMBOLS AND ABBREVIATIONS

A	point
a	area, acceleration
a_o	area of orifice
$da, \Delta a$	increment of area
B	point
$\mathbf{B}$	buoyant force
$\Delta \mathbf{B}$	increment of buoyant force
b	width, center of buoyancy
C	meter coefficient, point
C_c	coefficient of contraction
C_d	coefficient of discharge
C_v	coefficient of velocity
°C	degree Centigrade
c	distance, centroid
$dc, \Delta c$	increment of distance
c_p	specific heat at constant pressure
c_v	specific heat at constant volume
cfs	cubic feet/second
cos	cosine
cm	centimeter
cu ft	cubic feet
D	point
d	depth, diameter
E	specific energy
e	base of natural logarithm, 2.71828
°F	degree Fahrenheit
$\mathbf{F}$	force, frictional force
$\mathbf{F}_s$	shearing force
$\mathbf{F}_v$	vertical component of force

1

$\mathbf{F}_x$	component of force in x direction
$\mathbf{F}_y$	component of force in y direction
F.S.	factor of safety
f	coefficient of friction
ft	foot, feet
ft-lb	foot-pound
fps	feet/second
fps^2	feet/second per second
G	center of gravity
g	acceleration of gravity
gm	gram
gmm	gram-mass
gpm	gallons/minute
H	energy per pound of fluid, head, distance
Hg	mercury
H_t	total energy
$\bar{h}$	centroidal distance
h	head, height
h_a	added head
h_c	enlargement or contraction head loss
h_e	entrance head loss
h_f	head loss in pipe
h_x	exit head loss
hp	horsepower
I_c	moment of inertia with respect to centroidal axis
I_o	moment of inertia with respect to origin
in.	inches
K	roughness coefficient, bulk modulus
k	adiabatic constant, c_p/c_v
Kwhr	Kilowatt hour
L	length, distance
dL	increment of distance
lb	pounds, pounds
ln	logarithm to base e
M	mass, metacenter, moment
dM	increment of mass
dm	increment of distance in m direction
mgd	million gallons/day
N	normal force
N_r	Reynolds number
n	roughness coefficient, number of end contractions
dn	increment of distance in n direction

p	wetted perimeter
p, psig	gage pressure in pounds/square inch
$\bar{p}$, psia	absolute pressure in pounds/square inch
dp, Δp	increment of pressure
p_a	atmospheric pressure
pcf	pounds/cubic foot
psf	pounds/square foot
psi	pounds/square inch
Q	discharge (quantity per unit of time)
dQ, ΔQ	increment of discharge
q	discharge per unit width of channel, flow rate
R	gas constant, hydraulic radius,
$\mathbf{R}$	resultant force
$\Delta\mathbf{R}$	increment of resultant force
$\mathbf{R}_h$	component of resultant force in horizontal direction
$\mathbf{R}_v$	component of resultant force in vertical direction
$\mathbf{R}_x$	component of resultant force in x direction
$\mathbf{R}_y$	component of resultant force in y direction
r	radius
S_c	critical slope
S_g	specific gravity
s	slope
Δs	increment of distance
sec	second
sin	sine
T	absolute temperature
t	time
dt	increment of time
$\mathbf{U}$	uplift force
V	volume
ΔV	increment of volume
v	velocity
dv, Δv	increment of velocity
v_c	critical velocity
v_{fr}	relative final velocity
v_{fx}	final velocity in x direction
v_{ir}	relative intial velocity
v_{ix}	initial velocity in x direction
v_j	velocity of jet
v_v	velocity of vane
W	weight
dW	increment of weight

x	distance in x direction
$\bar{x}$	centroidal distance in x direction
dx, Δx	increment of distance in x direction
y	distance in y direction
$\bar{y}$	centroidal distance in y direction
dy, Δy	increment of distance in y direction
y_c	critical depth of channel
y_p	distance from moment center to center of pressure
y_R	moment arm of resultant force
z	distance in z direction
dz, Δz	increment of distance in z direction
$<$	less than
$\leq$	equal to or less than
$>$	greater than
$\geq$	equal to or greater than

GREEK SYMBOLS

α (alpha)	angle
γ (gamma)	specific weight
μ (mu)	coefficient of viscosity, coefficient of friction
ν (nu)	kinematic viscosity, μ/ρ
π (pi)	3.1416
ρ (rho)	density, variable radius
$\sum$ (sigma)	summation
σ (sigma)	surface tension
τ (tau)	shearing stress
θ (theta)	angle

Chapter 1

Fundamental Concepts

1-1 INTRODUCTION

A knowledge of the control and use of fluids was of considerable importance even in the ancient civilizations. This is evidenced by the aqueducts of Rome and the irrigation systems of Egypt and Babylonia. Hydraulic problems encountered in this early period of history were solved primarily by the method of trial-and-error.

Our present knowledge in the field of fluids has resulted from an accelerated increase during the past few centuries in the understanding of the laws and principles affecting the control and use of fluids. This knowledge has permitted the rational solution of many fluid problems that formerly were accepted solely on an empirical basis. However, our knowledge of these laws and principles is not yet complete; therefore, it is still necessary to depend to some extent on empirical solutions in a number of areas.

1-2 FLUID DEFINED

A fluid may be defined as a substance that does not resist shear forces when in the state of static equilibrium. For this reason, the fluid will take the shape of the container into which it is placed.

A liquid will take the shape of the container into which it is placed without changing its original bulk or volume since it will not necessarily fill the container.

A gas, on the other hand, will fill the container into which it is placed since it will expand or contract to conform to the size and shape of the container.

In general, for most pressures, including those used in this text, a liquid is considered incompressible. A gas, however, is readily compressible and its density will vary with the pressure and the temperature.

1-3 PROPERTIES

Before it is possible to arrive at a basic understanding of the laws and concepts relating to the study of fluids, it is desirable to have a knowledge of some of the properties that are used to express these laws and concepts. Among these are specific weight, density, specific gravity, viscosity, surface tension, and bulk modulus.

1-4 SPECIFIC WEIGHT

Specific weight is the weight per unit volume of a substance, and is usually taken as the weight per cubic foot. The specific weight of a substance varies with temperature. The specific weight, γ (gamma), of water at 4°C is approximately 62.4 pounds/cubic foot (pcf). This is the weight of water at its greatest density.

1-5 DENSITY

Density is defined as mass per unit volume of a substance. Usually, the volume is taken as one cubic foot. The density, ρ (rho), of water is expressed as

$$\rho = \frac{M}{V} = \frac{W}{gV} = \frac{\gamma}{g} = \frac{62.4}{32.2} = 1.94 \text{ slugs/cu ft,}$$

where M = the mass in slugs, or W/g
W = the total weight of the material, lb
V = the volume of the material, ft^3, and
g = the acceleration of gravity, 32.2 fps^2.

1-6 SPECIFIC GRAVITY

Specific gravity, S_g, of a substance is defined as the ratio of the density of the substance to the density of water at 4°C. Expressed as an equation,

$$S_g = \frac{\gamma_s/g}{\gamma_w/g} = \frac{\gamma_s}{\gamma_w},$$

where γ_s = the specific weight of the substance, and
          γ_w = the specific weight of water at 4°C.

The specific gravity can be expressed as the ratio of the specific weight of the substance to the specific weight of water at 4°C, or the total weight of the substance to the weight of an equal volume of water at 4°C. The weight per unit volume of water changes very little in the usual range of temperatures of tap water. Therefore, where a high degree of accuracy is not needed, water at room temperature is generally used in specific gravity determinations.

1-7 ABSOLUTE AND KINEMATIC VISCOSITIES

When a fluid is moving in a container or flowing in a pipe, particles or layers of particles of the fluid do not move at the same speed or velocity as adjacent particles or layers of particles. Even as solids in contact with each other and moving at different speeds create friction, in the same way fluids create friction, called shearing resistance, due to the varying velocities of the particles of fluid. Heavy fluids, such as heavy oils, offer more shearing resistance to flow than light oils. *The property which measures this shearing resistance is called the viscosity or absolute viscosity of the fluid.*

In order to find a relationship between the shearing resistance and the viscosity of the fluid, assume that the fluid is flowing slowly in a smooth pipe so that all the particles move in paths that are parallel to the sides of the pipe. This type of fluid flow is known as *laminar flow*. At the inner surface of the pipe, the particles of fluid cling to the pipe and have no velocity. As the distance from the inner surface of the pipe increases, the velocity of the fluid also increases until it becomes maximum at the center of the pipe, as shown in Fig. 1-1(a) and (b). Consider the two circular layers of particles of fluid in Fig. 1-1(b); the layers have their velocities separated by the distance Δc. The inner layer has a velocity Δv greater than the outer layer, as shown in Fig. 1-1(a). Since the inner layer is moving faster than the outer layer, shearing stresses are produced, designated τ (tau), due to the frictional resistance generated between the layers of particles. *The coefficient of viscosity, μ (mu), is defined as the ratio of the shearing stress to the rate of shearing strain,* or

$$\mu = \frac{\tau}{-\Delta v / \Delta c}$$

and

$$\tau = -\mu \frac{\Delta v}{\Delta c} \qquad\qquad (1\text{-}1)$$

where μ = the absolute viscosity of the fluid, lb-sec/ft², or slugs/ft-sec. The factor $\Delta v / \Delta c$ is negative because the velocity increases as the distance c decreases. The gravitational English system of units, used above, is generally used in engineering in the United States.

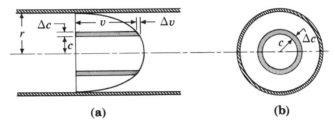

(a)   **(b)**

FIGURE 1-1

Viscosity of fluids is similar to the modulus of rigidity of solids. Table 1 gives the absolute viscosity of a number of common fluids.

The standard unit of measurement of viscosity in the metric absolute system is the poise, which has units of gram-mass per centimeter-seconds. One poise may be converted into the equivalent viscosity in the gravitational English system as follows:

$$1 \text{ gmm (gram-mass)} = 1 \frac{\text{gm-sec}^2}{32.2 \text{ ft}},$$

$$1 \text{ lb} = 454 \text{ gm},$$

$$1 \text{ ft} = 30.48 \text{ cm},$$

and

$$1 \text{ slug} = 1 \frac{\text{lb-sec}^2}{\text{ft}},$$

therefore,

$$1 \text{ poise} = 1\frac{\text{gmm}}{\text{cm-sec}} \times 1\,\text{gmm}\,\frac{\text{gm-sec}^2}{32.2 \text{ ft-cm-sec}} \times \frac{1 \text{ lb}}{454 \text{ gm}} \times \frac{30.48 \text{ cm}}{1 \text{ ft}} \times \frac{\text{slug-ft.}}{\text{lb sec}^2}.$$

After cancelling similar terms in the numerator and denominator, it is found that

$$1 \text{ poise} = 20.85(10^{-4}) \text{ slugs/ft-sec} = 20.85(10^{-4}) \text{ lb-sec/ft}^2.$$

In some problems of fluid mechanics, the *kinematic viscosity*, designated by the symbol v (nu), becomes a convenient factor to use. *The kinematic viscosity is the ratio of the absolute viscosity of the fluid to the density of the fluid*, or μ/ρ. The dimensions of kinematic viscosity are L^2/t, or length squared divided by time.

In the metric system, the standard unit of kinematic viscosity is called a stoke, and its units are centimeters squared per second. The centistoke is 0.01 stokes. The kinematic viscosity of water at 20°C is one centistoke.

One of several methods used to measure the viscosity of liquids is by use of the Saybolt-Universal viscosimeter. This instrument consists of a container of specified volume with a standard orifice in its bottom. The time in seconds required for the liquid in the filled container to flow out through the orifice is known as the *saybolt viscosity* of the liquid. Viscosity in seconds saybolt can be converted to stokes by the following empirical equations:

$$v = 0.00226t - \frac{1.95}{t}, \qquad \text{(when } t \leq 100\text{)}$$

or

$$v = 0.00220t - \frac{1.35}{t}, \qquad \text{(when } t > 100\text{)}$$

where v = viscosity in stokes, and
           t = viscosity in seconds saybolt.

Resistance to fluid flow in a pipe is due primarily to the viscosity of the fluid.

Table 1
PROPERTIES OF A FEW FLUIDS

Fluid	Temp. (°F)	Specific Weight lb/cu ft (γ)	Density slugs/cu ft (ρ)	Viscosity 10^{-6} slugs/ft-sec (μ)	Surface Tension 10^{-3} lb/ft (σ)	Vapor Pressure ft	Bulk Modulus 10^3 lb/in^2 (K)
Liquids							
Brine	60	71.8	1.15	35.0			
Castor Oil	32	60.8	1.898	149,000.0			
	59	60.3	1.874	31,000.0			
	68	59.9	1.863	20,600.0	2.1		
	100	58.9	1.833	5,460.0			
	150	57.8	1.796	1,260.0			
Crude Oil "A"	60	53.4	1.66	190.0	1.6		
Crude Oil "B"	60	57.8	1.80	1,900.0	2.5		
Crude Oil "C"	40	51.7	1.60	234.0			
	60	50.9	1.57	133.0			
	70	50.2	1.55	100.0			
Fuel Oil (Cracked)	70	56.9	1.77	110,000.0			
	100	56.1	1.74	13,900.0			
	120	55.6	1.73	6,100.0			
Fuel Oil (Furnace Oil)	60	53.0	1.65	124.0			
Gasoline "A"	60	42.4	1.32	6.5			
Gasoline "B"	60	46.8	1.45	15.0			
Glycerine	100	78.6	2.44	8,500.0			630
Kerosene "A"	60	50.6	1.57	40.0	1.6	0.40	
Lubricating Oil	40	56.4	1.75	8,350.0			
	60	55.9	1.74	3,260.0			
Medium	70	55.6	1.73	2,160.0	2.4		
	100	55.0	1.71	840.0			

Lubricating Oil S.A.E. 10	60	57.0	1.77	2,000.0			
Lubricating Oil S.A.E. 30	60	57.0	1.77	8,000.0			
Mobiloil "A"	100	57.4	1.77	2,100.0	2.5	0.68	217
Mercury	32	849.0	26.29	35.0		0.000001	
	68	843.0	26.20	33.0	35.7	0.000004	3750
	212	830.0	25.82	25.3		0.00092	
Water	32	62.42	1.940	37.46	5.18	0.204	284
	59	62.37	1.937	23.83	5.04	0.565	310
	68	62.30	1.934	20.98	4.98	0.774	318
	100	62.00	1.925	14.22	4.82	2.17	330
	150	61.20	1.901	9.04	4.54	8.56	328
	200	60.13	1.872	6.37	4.21	26.45	308
Gases							
Air	32	0.8071	0.00251	0.356			
	59*	0.07651	0.00238	0.3723			
	68	0.0749	0.00233	0.376			
	100	0.0712	0.00221	0.395			
Ammonia	50	0.0465	0.00145	2.0			
Carbon Dioxide	32	0.12341	0.00381	0.286			
Helium	32	0.01114	0.000345	0.392			
Hydrogen	32	0.00561	0.000175	0.179			
Nitrogen	32	0.07807	0.00242				
Oxygen	32	0.08921	0.00277	0.346			

* Known as *standard air* (15°C).

1-8   SURFACE TENSION

Surface tension is due to molecular attraction or the force of attraction that is present between molecules in a fluid. A molecule within a drop of liquid is attracted equally by the adjacent molecules that surround it. However, at the surface of the drop, the attraction is unbalanced and the resultant attraction is toward the center of the drop. Thus, if a drop of water is suspended in oil of approximately the same specific gravity, the drop of water will approximate the shape of a sphere.

A drop of mercury on a flat glass surface will tend to remain a sphere since the molecular attraction within the drop of mercury is greater than the attraction of gravity and is greater than the attraction between the glass and the mercury.

On the other hand, a drop of water on glass will be dispersed and form a thin sheet over the glass. This will take place because the molecular attraction within the drop is not sufficient to withstand the flattening effect of gravity and the attraction between the glass and the water.

The molecular attraction on the surface of liquids will produce tensile forces across any line on the surface of the liquid or at the boundary between the liquid and its container. The intensity of this tensile force per unit of length of this boundary, or line, is called the *surface tension,* σ (sigma). Thus,

$$\sigma = \mathbf{F}/L,$$

where $\mathbf{F}$ = the total tensile force, lb, and
           L = the length of the line on the surface or boundary, ft.

When a glass tube is immersed in a liquid, such as mercury, that does not wet the tube, the surface of the mercury will be depressed at all points of contact, as shown in Fig. 1-2(a). The attraction between the molecules of the mercury is greater than the attraction between the mercury and the glass tube so the mercury in the tube tends to assume a spherical surface.

When a tube is immersed in a liquid, such as water, that wets the tube, the liquid will rise in the tube, as shown in Fig. 1-2(b). The attraction between the glass and the water is greater than the attraction between the molecules of the water.

The height to which the liquid in the tube will rise depends on the surface tension, or force, developed at the line of contact of the liquid and the tube. A free-body diagram of the liquid above the liquid surface is shown in Fig. 1-2(c). The summation of the horizontal components of the surface tension is equal to zero. The summation of the vertical components of the surface tension is equal to the weight of the liquid above the liquid surface, or

$$\mathbf{F} \cos \theta = \mathbf{W}.$$

F is the resultant force due to all the surface tension at the line of contact between the liquid and the tube, and **W** is the weight of the liquid above

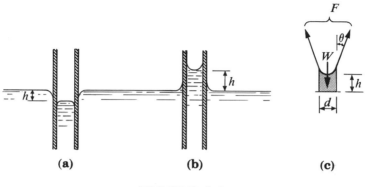

(a)   **(b)**   **(c)**

FIGURE 1-2

the surface of the liquid. This equation may be expressed in terms of the surface tension per foot of contact, σ, and the diameter of the tube. Thus,

$$\sigma \pi d \cos \theta = [(\pi d^2)/4] h \gamma,$$

or

$$h = \frac{4\sigma \cos \theta}{d\gamma}$$

where γ = the specific weight of the liquid, pcf
             d = the internal diameter of the tube, ft, and
             h = the height of the liquid above the surface, ft.

The contact angle between water and glass is approximately zero, so that $\cos \theta$ for water is 1.

1-9 BULK MODULUS

Since liquids compress very slightly under the pressures generally attained in most hydraulic structures, their compressibility is usually negligible. The resistance to change in volume of a confined liquid under pressure is referred to as *bulk modulus, which is defined as the ratio of the change in unit pressure to the corresponding change in unit volume under constant temperature.* That is,

$$K = \frac{\Delta p}{\Delta V / V}$$

where K = the bulk modulus of the liquid, psi
Δp = the change in unit pressure, psi
ΔV = the change in volume, in³.
V = the original volume, in³.

The bulk modulus of water under normal atmospheric conditions is approximately 300,000 psi.

Example 1-1.   Determine the specific weight, density, and specific gravity of a stone that weighs 1250 lb when weighed in air and displaces 458 lb of water when immersed in a tank of water. The water is at 68°F.

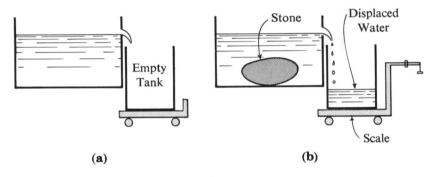

(a)   **(b)**

FIGURE 1-3

Solution: Figures 1-3(a) and (b) show the tanks and water before and after the stone was immersed. The volume of water displaced by the stone is the weight of the water displaced divided by the weight of 1 cu ft of that water. At 68°F the weight is 62.3 pcf. Therefore, since the volume of the water displaced is equal to the volume of the stone,

$$\text{Volume of stone} = \frac{458}{62.3} = 7.35 \text{ cu ft.}$$

The specific weight, γ, of the stone is

$$\gamma = \frac{1250}{7.35} = 170 \text{ pcf.}$$

Since the density of the stone can be expressed by γ/g,

$$\rho = \frac{170}{32.2} = 5.28 \text{ slugs/cu ft.}$$

The specific gravity, S_g, of the stone is its weight divided by the weight of an equal volume of water at 4°C. Therefore,

$$S_g = \frac{1250}{7.35(62.4)} = 2.73 \text{ (dimensionless).}$$

Example 1-2. Two parallel plates, each 4 ft square, are submerged horizontally 4 in. apart in water at 68°F. If a horizontal force of ¼ lb is applied to one of the plates, what relative velocity of the plates will be maintained. Neglect all forces except the force due to the viscosity of the water.

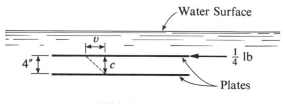

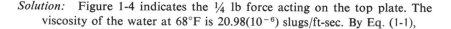

FIGURE 1-4

Solution: Figure 1-4 indicates the ¼ lb force acting on the top plate. The viscosity of the water at 68°F is $20.98(10^{-6})$ slugs/ft-sec. By Eq. (1-1),

$$\tau = -\mu(\Delta v/\Delta c).$$

Assuming that $\Delta v/\Delta c$ remains constant, that is, the velocity of the fluid varies directly with the distance c,

$$\tau = -\mu(v/c).$$

Since

$$F = \tau a = (-\mu v/c)a$$

therefore

$$v = Fc/\mu a.$$

Substituting values,

$$v(\text{relative}) = \frac{1}{4}\frac{1}{16}\frac{1}{3}\frac{10^6}{20.98} = 248 \text{ fps.}$$

Example 1-3. Determine the pressure on the inside of a drop of water 0.10 in. in diameter at a temperature of 68°F.

Solution: Figure 1-5 is a free-body diagram of one-half of the drop of water with the forces indicated. The surface tension from Table 1 is $4.98(10^{-3})$ lb/ft. By $\sum F_x = 0$,

$$pa = \sigma L$$

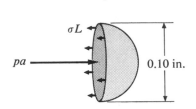

FIGURE 1-5

where L is the circumference of the drop of water. Therefore,

$$p\pi d^2/4 = \sigma\pi d$$

and

$$p = \frac{4\sigma}{d} = \frac{4(4.98)12}{10^3(0.10)} = \frac{239}{100} = 2.39 \text{ psi.}$$

PROBLEMS

1-1. A substance has a volume of 3.30 cu ft and weighs 115.5 lb. Determine (a) its specific weight, and (b) its density.

1-2. A substance has a density of 1.75 slugs/cu ft. Determine (a) its specific weight, and (b) its specific gravity.

1-3. A substance has a specific weight of 57.0 pcf. Determine (a) its specific gravity, and (b) its density.

1-4. Two parallel plates, each 2 ft square, are separated by 4 inches of mercury at 68°F. Determine the force that is needed to maintain a relative velocity of 15 fps between the plates, considering only the viscosity of the mercury.

1-5. Two parallel plates, each 3 ft square, are separated by 6 inches of medium lubricating oil at 70°F. If a force of 0.05 lb, parallel to the plates, is applied to one of the plates, what relative velocity will occur considering only the viscosity of the oil?

1-6. Two parallel plates, each 3 ft in diameter, are separated by 3 inches of water at 32°F. Determine the force applied to and parallel to one of the plates to produce a relative velocity of 5 fps.

1-7. How high will water at 100°F rise in a tube 0.02 inches in diameter?

1-8. How high will water at 68°F rise in a tube 0.05 inches in diameter?

1-9. What is the pressure on the inside of a rain drop 0.12 inches in diameter at a temperature of 32°F?

1-10. What is the pressure on the inside of a soap bubble 1 in. in diameter if the surface tension is 50 percent of that of water at 68°F?

1-11. The inner cylinder, shown in Fig. P 1-11, has a diameter of 3 in. The gap between cylinders is 0.200 in. Determine the torque required to rotate the cylinder at 180 rpm if a space, 12 in. long, between cylinders is filled with kerosene at 60°F. Neglect bearing friction.

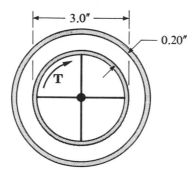

FIGURE P 1-11

1-12. Solve Prob. 1-11 if the fluid is mercury at 68°F.

1-13. What is the kinematic viscosity (in stokes) of an oil having a saybolt viscosity of 180 sec?

1-14. What is the kinematic viscosity (in stokes) of an oil having a saybolt viscosity of 80 sec?

1-15. Determine the saybolt viscosity of crude oil "B" at 60°F.

1-16. Determine the saybolt viscosity of furnace oil at 60°F.

1-17. Determine the kinematic viscosity of air at 59°F in the fps system.

1-18. Under what conditions will the kinematic viscosity (in stokes) be numerically equal to the absolute viscosity in poises?

1-19. By what number must the kinematic viscosity (in stokes) be multiplied to convert it to the fps system?

1-10   COMPRESSIBLE GASES

Gases are readily compressed and behave according to the general gas law for which the basic equation is

$$\bar{p}V = WRT \qquad \text{or} \qquad \bar{p} = \gamma RT$$

where $\bar{p}$ = the absolute pressure, psi
           V = volume, in.^{3}
           W = weight, lb
           T = the absolute temperature, °Rankine, and
           R = a constant, ft/°Rankine.

The Rankine temperature is determined by adding the Fahrenheit temperature to 459.4.

For isothermal conditions, that is, when there is no change in temperature during compression or expansion of the gas, Boyle's law applies. This law states

$$\bar{p}_1 V_1 = \bar{p}_2 V_2 = \text{a constant.} \tag{1-2}$$

This implies that heat is lost in the process of compression in order to maintain the constant temperature, and heat flows into the gas during the expansion process.

Adiabatic expansion or compression means that there is no heat transfer, neither loss or gain, through the boundary of the gas. Therefore, as compression takes place the temperature will rise, and as expansion takes place the temperature of the gas will drop. The adiabatic equation is

$$\bar{p}_1 V_1^k = \bar{p}_2 V_2^k = \text{a constant} \tag{1-3}$$

where k is the adiabatic constant[1] (Table 2).

TABLE 2

Gas	R Ft/°Rankine	k
Acetylene	58.8	1.28
Air	53.3	1.41
Ammonia	89.5	1.32
Carbon Dioxide	34.9	1.31
Helium	387.0	1.66
Hydrogen	767.0	1.41
Nitrogen	55.1	1.40
Oxygen	48.3	1.39

1. The symbol k is the ratio of specific heat at constant pressure, c_p, to specific heat at constant volume, c_v. The specific heat at constant pressure is the number of Btu's required to raise the temperature of 1 lb of gas 1° F when its pressure is held constant. The specific heat at constant volume is the number of Btu's required to raise the temperature of 1 lb of gas 1° F when its volume is held constant.

Charles' law states that the volume of a given mass of gas varies directly as its temperature when it is held at constant pressure. That is,

$$V/T = \text{a constant.}$$

Substituting this constant into Eq. (1-2) gives,

$$(\bar{p}_1 V_1)/T_1 = (\bar{p}_2 V_2)/T_2 = WR = \text{a constant.} \tag{1-4}$$

The absolute pressure, $\bar{p}$, is the atmospheric pressure (14.7 psi at sea level) plus the applied gage pressure. The absolute temperature is the Fahrenheit temperature plus 459.4 or the Centigrade temperature plus 273.

Example 1-4. The air in an engine cylinder occupies 240 cu in. at 5.3 psi gage, before compression. If the temperature of the air remains constant, determine the air pressure (gage) when the volume of air in the cylinder is compressed to 120 cu in.

Solution: Since the temperature of the air in the cylinder does not change during compression, Boyle's law applies. Thus,

$$\bar{p}_1 V_1 = \bar{p}_2 V_2.$$

Substituting the known values gives

$$(14.7 + 5.3)240 = \bar{p}_2(120).$$

Therefore,

$$\bar{p}_2 = \frac{20(240)}{120} = 40 \text{ psia}$$

and

$$p_2(\text{gage}) = 40 - 14.7 = 25.3 \text{ psig.}$$

Example 1-5. Assume that adiabatic conditions apply to the compression of the air in Ex. 1-4. Determine the air pressure (gage) when the air is compressed to 120 cu in.

Solution: Since no heat is lost in the compression of the air, Eq. (1-3) applies. Thus,

$$\bar{p}_1 V_1^k = \bar{p}_2 V_2^k$$

where k for air is 1.41. Substituting known values into the adiabatic equation gives,

$$20(240)^{1.41} = \bar{p}_2(120)^{1.41}$$

or

$$\bar{p}_2 = 20(2)^{1.41} = 20(2.64) = 53.2 \text{ psia.}$$

Then,
$$p_2(\text{gage}) = 53.2 - 14.7 = 38.5 \text{ psig}.$$

Example 1-6. Assume that the air in Ex. 1-4 has a temperature of 60°F before being compressed and a temperature of 90°F after compression. Determine the final gage pressure.

Solution: In this case, the absolute temperatures before and after compression are readily available. Therefore, the equation determined from Charles' law applies, and
$$(\bar{p}_1 V_1)/T_1 = (\bar{p}_2 V_2)/T_2.$$

The initial absolute temperature is
$$T_1 = 60 + 460 = 520°F,$$

and the final absolute temperature is
$$T_2 = 90 + 460 = 550°F.$$

Therefore, substituting known values into Eq. (1-4), gives
$$\frac{20(240)}{520} = \frac{\bar{p}_2(120)}{550}$$

and
$$\bar{p}_2 = \frac{40(550)}{520} = 42.3 \text{ psia(absolute)}.$$

Therefore,
$$p_2 = 42.3 - 14.7 = 27.6 \text{ psig(gage)}.$$

PROBLEMS

1-20. Three cu ft of air at 14.7 psia are compressed to 2 cu ft under constant temperature. Determine the gage pressure in psi of the compressed air.

1-21. Assume the temperature of the air in Prob. 1-20 is changed from 68°F to 100°F in the compression process. Determine the absolute pressure in psi of the compressed air.

1-22. Assume that no heat is lost in the process of compressing the air in Prob. 1-20. Determine the pressure in psia of the compressed air.

1-23. One cu ft of hydrogen gas at 14.7 psia is compressed to 0.60 cu ft, the temperature being kept constant. Determine the gage pressure in psi of the compressed gas.

1-24. Two cu ft of oxygen at 30 psia are compressed to 1 cu ft. What is the absolute pressure if no heat is lost in the compression process?

1-25. Four cu ft of carbon dioxide at 200 psia is allowed to expand to 12 cu ft under adiabatic conditions. What is the absolute pressure of the expanded gas?

1-26. Five cu ft of helium gas at 4°C and 25 psi gage pressure at sea level is compressed to 3 cu ft and the temperature is raised to 68°C. Determine the final gage pressure required to compress the gas.

1-27. A tank contains 3 lb of air at 68°F and 294 psia. What is its volume?

1-28. How much lighter is nitrogen at 14.7 psia and 32°F than at 44.1 psia and 96°F?

1-29. At what pressure must ammonia be stored at 50°F so that it will have a temperature of −50°F when it is expanded adiabatically to 14.7 psia?

1-30. A liquid, when subjected to 2500 psi pressure, decreases in volume 3.0 percent. What is its bulk modulus of elasticity?

1-31. A closed steel tank, assumed rigid, has a volume of 15 cu ft. How many pounds of water at 32°F does it hold at 1200 psi? The bulk modulus of elasticity of water is 300,000 psi.

1-32. Determine the viscosity of castor oil at 59°F in poises.

1-33. An oil has a viscosity of 360 poises. Determine its viscosity in the fps system.

1-34. A 6-in.-diameter sleeve revolves on an axle at 500 rpm with a radial clearance of 0.0025 in. Determine the torque in in-lb/ft of sleeve required to overcome oil resistance if μ of the oil is 2.0 poises.

Chapter 2

Fluids at Rest

2-1 INTRODUCTION

When fluids remain in equilibrium, they develop forces on the containing receptacle due to the gravitational pull of the earth on the fluid. In order to properly design the containing vessel, these forces must be evaluated.

The total pressure, or force, exerted by a fluid in equilibrium is a vector quantity and as such has magnitude, direction, and point of application, or position of line of action. Generally, the term pressure is used to indicate the intensity of the pressure at a point in a fluid. That is, the pressure per unit area, expressed usually as pounds per square inch (psi). That is,

$$p_{\text{avg}} = \mathbf{F}/a$$

where $\mathbf{F}$ = the total fluid force acting on the area a, and
p = the average pressure per unit of area.

2-2 DIRECTION OF PRESSURE

The direction of the pressure of a fluid in equilibrium on a plane in the fluid or at its boundary is always perpendicular to the plane or boundary, as shown in Fig. 2-1(a). If the forces were not normal to the bounding surface or plane in the fluid, they would have components perpendicular and parallel to the plane or bounding surface. This is illustrated for a single force in Fig. 2-1(b). However, this parallel component cannot exist in equilibrium by itself since it would produce flow or motion of the fluid, and a fluid at rest has no flow or motion. Therefore, the force or pressure exerted by a fluid is always normal to the surface of the containing vessel.

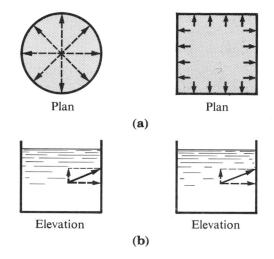

Plan   Plan

(a)

Elevation   Elevation

(b)

FIGURE 2-1

2-3 PRESSURE AT A POINT IN A FLUID

The intensity of pressure at a point in a fluid is the same on any plane through that point. For example, assume a small triangular wedge of fluid at a given point in a vessel, as shown in Fig. 2-2. Since the liquid is in equilibrium, and $\sum \mathbf{F}_x = 0$,

$$p_1 \, \Delta y \, \Delta z = p_3 \, \Delta z \, \Delta s \sin \theta.$$

Since

$$\Delta y = \Delta s \sin \theta \qquad \text{and} \qquad \Delta s = \Delta y / \sin \theta,$$

$$p_1 \, \Delta y \, \Delta z = p_3 \, \Delta y \, \Delta z.$$

By cancellation,

$$p_1 = p_3.$$

Also, by $\Sigma \, \mathbf{F}_y = 0$,

$$p_2 \, \Delta x \, \Delta z = p_3 \, \Delta z \, \Delta s \cos \theta.$$

Again,

$$\Delta x = \Delta s \cos \theta \quad \text{and} \quad \Delta s = \Delta x / \cos \theta.$$

Therefore,

$$p_2 \, \Delta x \, \Delta z = p_3 \, \Delta x \, \Delta z.$$

By cancellation,

$$p_2 = p_3.$$

Therefore,

$$p_1 = p_2 = p_3. \tag{2-1}$$

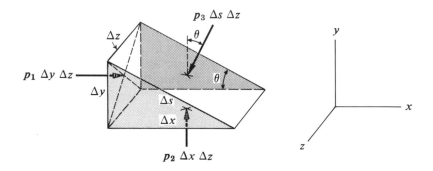

FIGURE 2-2

Since θ is taken as any angle so that the result does not depend on a specific angle, the unit pressure at any specified point in a fluid at rest is always the same in all directions.

2-4 PRESSURE VARIATION IN A FLUID

Variations in pressure occur both in gases and in liquids. *The pressure in a fluid is dependent on the depth of the fluid and the specific gravity of the fluid.*

Assume a free-body diagram of a differential cubical element of a fluid, as shown in Fig. 2-3. The adjacent fluid will exert normal pressures on the faces of the cubical element. The y axis is taken as positive downward and the pressure, p, is assumed to increase in the positive direction. By $\Sigma \, \mathbf{F}_y = 0$,

$$\gamma \, \Delta x \, \Delta y \, \Delta z - (p + \Delta p) \, \Delta x \, \Delta z + p \, \Delta x \, \Delta z = 0.$$

By cancelling $\Delta x \, \Delta z$ and similar negative and positive values,

$$\Delta p = \gamma \, \Delta y. \qquad (2\text{-}2)$$

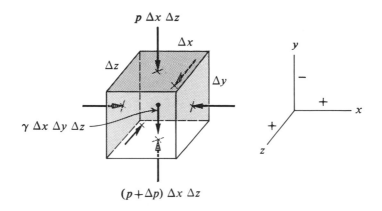

FIGURE 2-3

2-5 PRESSURE IN A LIQUID

If we assume that the specific weight of liquids do not change significantly due to the normal change of pressures and temperatures encountered in most hydraulic situations, the pressure at any point below the surface of a liquid varies directly with the depth, h, of the liquid, and thus Eq. (2-2) can be written,

$$p = \gamma h. \qquad (2\text{-}3)$$

In this equation, p is called the gage pressure since the atmospheric pressure is not considered in its calculation.

If the atmospheric pressure at the surface of the liquid is considered, the equation becomes

$$\bar{p} = p_a + \gamma h \qquad (2\text{-}4)$$

where $\bar{p}$ = the absolute pressure at a point a distance h below the surface of the liquid, and
p_a = the atmospheric pressure at the surface of the liquid.

Example 2-1. Mercury at 32°F stands at a depth of 4 ft in a storage tank.

Determine **(a)** the pressure (psig) at the bottom of the tank, and **(b)** the absolute pressure (psia) at the bottom of the tank. The tank is located at sea level.

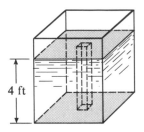

FIGURE 2-4

Solution: Figure 2-4 is a sketch of the tank showing an imaginary column of mercury 4 ft high and 1 sq in. in cross section. The specific gravity of mercury is 13.6. Substituting known values into Eq. (2-3) gives

$$p = \gamma h = \frac{13.6(62.4)}{144} \, 4 = 13.6(0.433)4 = 23.6 \text{ psig,}$$

which is the gage pressure at the bottom of the tank.

Since the atmospheric pressure at sea level is 14.7 psi, the absolute pressure at the bottom of the tank is

$$\bar{p} = 14.7 + 23.6 = 38.3 \text{ psia (absolute pressure).}$$

2-6 PRESSURE HEAD

Sometimes it is desirable to express the pressure in terms of the height of a column of fluid that will produce that pressure. *The height of a column of liquid that produces the pressure is termed the pressure head.* That is, since

$$p = \gamma h,$$

therefore,

$$h = p/\gamma \tag{2-5}$$

where h = pressure head, ft of fluid
γ = specific weight of that fluid, and
p = intensity of pressure.

If p is in psi, γ is the specific weight of a column of liquid 1 ft high and 1 sq in. in cross section. For example,

$$h = \frac{p(\text{psf})/144}{\gamma(\text{pcf})/144} = \frac{p(\text{psi})}{\gamma(\text{lb/sq in.-ft})}.$$

Since the specific weight of a column of water 1 sq. in. in cross section and 1 ft high is

$$\gamma = \frac{62.4}{144} = 0.433 \text{ lb/sq in.-ft,}$$

$$h(\text{ft}) = \frac{p(\text{psi})}{0.433}.$$

This gives the pressure head in feet of water.

If another liquid is used, the pressure head in feet of that liquid is

$$h = \frac{p(\text{psi})}{0.433(S_g)}$$

where S_g is the specific gravity of that liquid.

For example, to convert 14.7 psi atmospheric pressure into pressure head in inches of mercury, $S_g = 13.6$,

$$h(\text{ft}) = \frac{14.7}{0.433(13.6)} = \frac{14.7}{5.89} = 2.496 \text{ ft of mercury.}$$

Then, $2.496(12) = 29.9$ inches of mercury.

Example 2-2. A gage pressure of 18 psi is equivalent to how many (a) feet of oil, $(S_g = 0.90)$, and (b) inches of mercury?

Solution: Since $h = p/\gamma$,

(a)
$$h = \frac{18}{0.433(0.90)} = 46.2 \text{ ft of oil, and}$$

(b)
$$h = \frac{18(12)}{0.433(13.6)} = \frac{216}{5.89} = 36.7 \text{ in. of mercury.}$$

2-7 VAPOR PRESSURE

If a long vertical tube is filled with a liquid, then inverted, and the open end placed in a pan of the liquid, the liquid will drop in the tube until the weight of the column of liquid in the tube balances the atmospheric pressure on the surface of the liquid in the pan, as shown in Fig. 2-5(a). If no air is entrained in the tube in the inverting process a perfect vacuum will result above the liquid in the tube. The height of the liquid column will be

$$h = p_a/\gamma$$

where p_a = the atmospheric pressure, and
    γ = the specific weight of the liquid.

However, the enclosed vacuum will remain as such only temporarily since the evaporation of the liquid in the tube will take place rapidly at first and then more slowly until a balance is reached between the molecules of liquid leaving the liquid and the molecules of liquid returning to the liquid in the tube. This evaporation at the surface of the liquid in the tube will increase the pressure in the vacuum, thereby creating only a partial vacuum. Due to the increased pressure above the liquid in the tube, the liquid surface will drop slightly, as indicated in Fig. 2-5(b). The difference

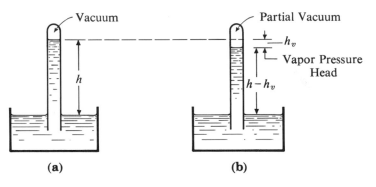

FIGURE 2-5

in heights of the surfaces of the liquid in the tube is the pressure head produced by the *vapor pressure*. As the temperature of the liquid rises, the vapor pressure rises. Values for vapor pressures for various liquids are given in Table 1.

Since the vapor pressure of mercury at ordinary temperatures is negligible (0.000004 ft at 68°F), mercury is used almost exclusively in barometers to determine the absolute atmospheric pressure. Vapor pressure may become an item for consideration when pumping water under high suction heads. Leakages and other inefficiencies of the pump usually reduce the suction head to a maximum of approximately 22 ft.

Example 2-3. Determine the maximum theoretical height to which water at 150°F may be raised by a vacuum at sea level.

Solution: The specific weight of water at 150°F is 61.2 pcf. Under a perfect vacuum, the water will rise

$$h = \frac{p}{\gamma} = \frac{14.7(144)}{61.2} = 34.59 \text{ ft.}$$

The vapor pressure of water at 150°F, taken from Table 1, is 8.56 ft. Therefore, the maximum height that the water will rise is

$$h_{max} = 34.59 - 8.56 = 26.03 \text{ ft.}$$

PROBLEMS

2-1. Water at 68°F stands at a depth of 12 ft in a reservoir. Determine the pressure in psi at the bottom of the reservoir.

2-2. An open vertical pipe, 12 in. in diameter and 6 ft high, is filled with glycerine at 100°F. Determine the pressure in psi at the bottom of the pipe.

2-3. Water at 68°F is to be supplied to a city by a standpipe. If the pressure at the hydrants must be 70 psig, determine the required elevation of the water surface in the standpipe.

2-4. How high a column of gasoline ($\gamma = 42.4$ pcf) would be required to give the same pressure as 24 in. of mercury at 68°F?

2-5. How high a column of water at 32°F would give the same pressure as 30 in. of mercury at the same temperature?

2-6. What is the average barometric reading (inches of mercury) at an elevation of 8000 ft? See Table 3.

2-7. What is the gage pressure in psi 300 ft below the surface of the ocean if the specific gravity of the water is 1.03?

2-8. Determine the pressure in psf on the face of a dam 30 ft below the water surface.

2-9. What height of a column of mercury will cause a pressure of 25 psi?

2-10. What height of a column of mercury will exert the same pressure as a column of oil 20 ft high (S_g of oil $= 0.85$)?

2-11. Assume the unit weight of air to be constant at 0.0765 pcf. Determine the approximate decrease in pressure in psi corresponding to a rise in elevation of 2000 ft.

2-12. Determine the pressure in psi 5 ft below the surface of a liquid, having a density of 1.76 slugs/cu ft, if the pressure on the surface of the liquid is 10 psi.

2-8 PRESSURES IN GASES

Equation (2-3), $p = \gamma h$, was derived on the assumption that the specific weight of the liquid remains constant, which gives satisfactory results for the limited distance, h, necessary in most hydraulic situations. However, since gases are readily compressible, the specific weight may be considered to be constant without serious error only for very small values of h. Where large values of h are involved, the variation of γ may be determined from the use of the general gas law, which is,

$$\bar{p}V = WRT$$

or

$$\bar{p} = \gamma RT \tag{2-6}$$

where $\bar{p}$ = the absolute pressure
γ = the specific weight
R = a constant, ft/°R, and
T = the absolute temperature, °R.

The equation for the absolute pressure anywhere in a gas, if we assume no change in temperature, with point 2 below point 1, and h equal to the vertical distance between points 1 and 2, is,

$$\bar{p}_1 = \bar{p}_2 e^{-h/RT} \tag{2-7}$$

or

$$\bar{p}_2 = \bar{p}_1 e^{h/RT} \tag{2-8}$$

in which e is the base of natural logarithms, or approximately 2.72.

Note: The following discussion involves calculus.

Equation (2-8) is derived as follows: Substituting Eq. (2-6), $\bar{p} = \gamma RT$, into Equation (2-2), $\Delta p = \gamma\,\Delta y$, gives,

$$\frac{\bar{p}}{RT} = \lim_{\Delta y \to 0} \frac{\Delta p}{\Delta y} = \frac{dp}{dy}.$$

Therefore,

$$RT\frac{dp}{\bar{p}} = dy.$$

Assuming no change in the temperature, T,

$$RT\int_{\bar{p}_1}^{\bar{p}_2} \frac{dp}{\bar{p}} = \int_{y_1}^{y_2} dy.$$

By integration,

$$RT(\ln \bar{p}_2 - \ln \bar{p}_1) = y_2 - y_1 = h$$

where $h = y_2 - y_1$.
Therefore,

$$RT \ln \frac{\bar{p}_2}{\bar{p}_1} = h, \quad \text{and} \quad p_2 = \bar{p}_1 e^{h/RT}. \tag{2-8}$$

TABLE 3

VARIATION IN ATMOSPHERIC PRESSURE WITH ALTITUDE

Altitude above Sea Level (ft)	Pressure (psi)	Altitude above Sea Level (ft)	Pressure (psi)
0	14.7	5,280	12.1
1,000	14.2	6,000	11.8
2,000	13.7	7,000	11.3
3,000	13.2	8,000	10.9
4,000	12.7	9,000	10.5
5,000	12.2	10,000	10.1

Where temperature variations occur, the rate of change of temperature would need to be considered such as the rate of change that occurs in the earth's atmosphere.

Example 2-4.   The air pressure is 10.1 psia at an elevation of 10,000 ft above sea level. Determine the air pressure at sea level. Assume the temperature of the air remains constant at 0°F.

Solution: The constant R for air is 53.3, and the absolute temperature (Rankine) is 459.4 degrees. Therefore, since,

$$\bar{p}_2 = \bar{p}_1 e^{h/RT}$$

$$\bar{p}_2 = 10.1(2.72)^{10,000/53.3(459.4)} = 10.1(2.72)^{1/2.452}$$

$$\bar{p}_2 = 10.1(1.504) = 15.2 \text{ psia}.$$

PROBLEMS

2-13.   Under isothermal conditions, determine the atmospheric pressure for standard air at an elevation of 8000 ft above sea level.

2-14. In an isothermal atmosphere, composed of oxygen at 32°F, determine the absolute pressure 5000 ft above a point at which the atmospheric pressure is 14.7 psia.

2-15. If a balloon contains 1200 cu ft of helium at sea level at 59°F, what will be the volume of the helium at an elevation of 40,000 ft? Assume isothermal conditions.

2-9 PRESSURE MEASURING DEVICES

Pressures in pipe lines and tanks may be measured by the use of gages and manometers. The Bourdon gage, shown in Fig. 2-6, can be calibrated and corrections made by adjusting the linkage connecting the end of the Bourdon tube and the indicating hand.

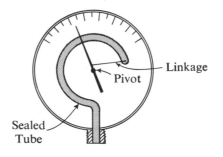

The Bourdon Gage.

FIGURE 2-6

An open-end manometer, as shown in Fig. 2-7, *is called a piezometer tube.* One end is open to the atmosphere and the other end is connected to a pipe or tank containing the liquid that produces the pressure. The pressure increases as the depth increases and diminishes as the depth diminishes. For example, refer to Fig. 2-7(a). The pressure in the pipe is

$$p_A = \gamma h = 0.433(S_g)h.$$

The accuracy of the pressure reading of a piezometer tube may be increased by sloping the tube. By inclining the tube at an angle of 30°, as shown in Fig. 2-7(b), the scale reading is doubled for the same vertical head shown in Fig. 2-7(a).

Where each end of the manometer is attached to pressure points, the difference in pressure between the two points is measured. Such a manometer is called a differential manometer. See Fig. 2-8. In order to determine the difference in pressure between points A and B (Fig. 2-8), an equation is written for the increase and decrease in pressure in the tube between points A and B, starting at one end of the connecting manometer tube.

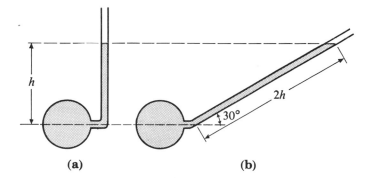

(a)   (b)

FIGURE 2-7

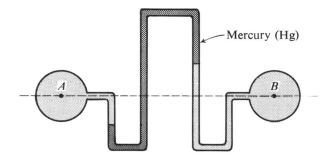

FIGURE 2-8

Example 2-5. An open vertical manometer is attached to a pipe containing gasoline ($\gamma = 46.8$ pcf) under a pressure of 12 psig. How high above the center of the pipe will the gasoline rise in the piezometer tube?

Solution: Since $h = p/\gamma$,

$$h = \frac{12(144)}{46.8} = 36.9 \text{ ft.}$$

Example 2-6. In Fig. 2-9, pipe A contains water and pipe B contains oil.

The specific gravity of the oil is 0.80. If the pressure in pipe B is 16 psig, determine the gage pressure in pipe A.

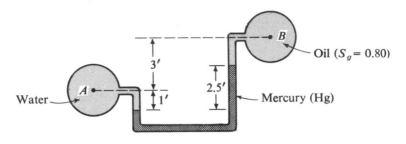

FIGURE 2-9

Solution: Start at pipe A and write a manometer equation through the manometer tube to pipe B. Thus,

$$p_A + 0.433(1) - 13.6(0.433)2.5 - 0.8(0.433)1.5 = 16$$

$$p_A = 16 + 14.72 + 0.52 - 0.43$$

$$p_A = 30.81 \text{ psig.}$$

Example 2-7. Determine the new differential reading on the mercury manometer, measured along the sloping tube, shown in Fig. 2-10, if the pressure in pipe A is increased 10 psi and the pressure in pipe B remains at 6 psi. Both pipes contain water.

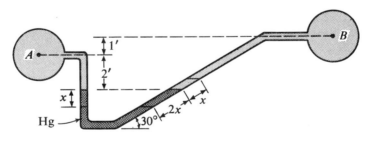

FIGURE 2-10

Solution: First write an equation for the pressure in pipe A before the pressure is increased. Thus,

$$p_A + 2(0.433) - 3(0.433) = 6.0.$$

Now, write an equation for the pressure in pipe A after the pressure is increased 10 psi. The mercury will move up in the sloping tube, as shown in Fig. 2-10. Thus,

$$(p_A + 10) + 0.433(2 + x) - 13.6(0.433)\left(x + \frac{x}{2}\right) - 0.433\left(3 - \frac{x}{2}\right) = 6.$$

Subtract the first equation from the second and solve for x. The difference is

$$10 + 0.433(x) - 13.6(0.433)\frac{3x}{2} + 0.433\left(\frac{x}{2}\right) = 0.$$

Solving for x,

$$8.18x = 10 \quad \text{and} \quad x = 1.222 \text{ ft.}$$

Therefore, the new differential reading, measured along the sloping tube, is

$$d = 1.222 + 2(1.222) = 3.67 \text{ ft.}$$

PROBLEMS

2-16. An open-end mercury manometer is attached to pipe A containing a liquid $(S_g = 0.75)$ under a pressure of 40 psig, as shown in Fig. P 2-16. Determine the differential mercury reading, h.

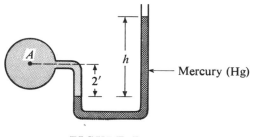

FIGURE P 2-16

2-17. If the pressure in the pipe in Prob. 2-16 is increased 10 psi, determine the new differential mercury reading.

2-18. If the pressure in the pipe in Fig. P 2-18 is increased 5 psi above the pressure indicated, determine the new differential mercury reading.

2-19. Two pipes at the same elevation contain oil $(S_g = 0.90)$ and are connected by a U-tube manometer containing mercury, as shown in Fig. P 2-19. Determine the difference in pressure in the two pipes when the differential mercury reading is 15 in.

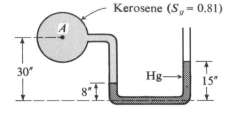

FIGURE P 2-18

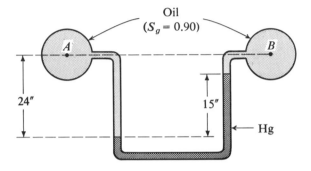

FIGURE P 2-19

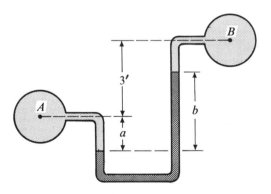

FIGURE P 2-20

2-20. In Fig. P 2-20, determine the pressure head in pipe A if the pressure in pipe B is 24 psig and both pipes contain water ($a = 12$ in. and $b = 24$ in.).

2-21. If, in Fig. P 2-20, pipe A contains water under a pressure of 18 psi, and pipe B contains an acid ($S_g = 1.75$) under a pressure of 12 psi, determine the differential mercury reading. Assume $a = 1.5$ ft.

2-22. Determine the new differential mercury reading on the manometer of Fig. P 2-22 if the pressure in pipe *A* is increased 8 psi and the pressure in pipe *B* remains unchanged.

2-23. Determine the pressure in pipe *A* of Fig. P 2-23 when the scale reading on the sloping pipe is 30 in. of mercury.

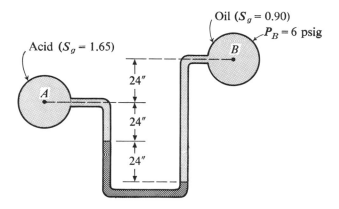

FIGURE P 2-22

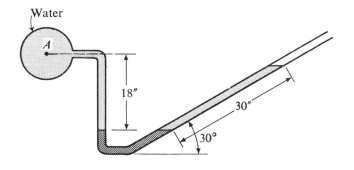

FIGURE P 2-23

2-24. Determine the new vertical differential reading in inches on the mercury manometer in Fig. P 2-24 if the pressure in pipe *A* is increased 6 psi and the pressure in pipe *B* remains at 10 psig.

2-25. A box, 1 ft square and 6 ft high, is closed at one end. If it is submerged in water with the open end down until the closed end extends 1 ft above the water surface, as shown in Fig. P 2-25, determine the gage pressure in the box.

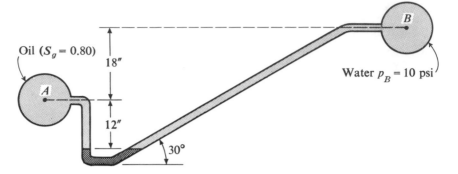

FIGURE P 2-24

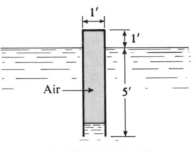

FIGURE P 2-25

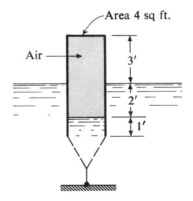

FIGURE P 2-27

2-26.   Determine the pressure in the box of Prob. 2-25 when the closed end of the box is even with the water surface.

2-27.   The hollow, thin-walled float of Fig. P 2-27 is held in a vertical position by the anchor rope. The float is open at the bottom and weighs 100 lb.

What will be the tension in the rope if the water surface outside the float rises 5 ft?

2-28. When the tank of Fig. P 2-28 is empty, the mercury is level with the bottom of the tank. If the manometer tube is closed at point A and the tank is filled with water to a depth of 20 ft, determine the differential mercury reading in ft. Assume no change in temperature.

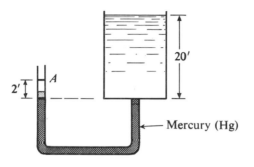

FIGURE P 2-28

2-10 FORCES EXERTED BY LIQUIDS

A knowledge of the forces exerted by liquids on their containers, such as dams, reservoirs, sea walls, hydraulic cylinders, and other devices developed for the retention of the liquids, is necessary for their correct and safe design. As stated in Sec. 2-2, the force, or pressure, exerted by a liquid at rest is always normal to the wall of the containing vessel. The evaluation of the magnitude and position of application of the resultant pressure on submerged areas may be determined by the *pressure diagram method* or by rationally developed formulas.

2-11 THE PRESSURE DIAGRAM METHOD—PLANE SURFACES

The pressure exerted by a liquid on a submerged plane surface constitutes a distributed load or force. The distributed load is composed of a number of concentrated forces, each acting over a small area. These concentrated forces constitute a parallel system of forces. The magnitude of the resultant pressure is the algebraic sum of the forces and is equal to the volume of the pressure diagram. The resultant pressure acts perpendicular to the plane surface and passes through the centroid of the volume of the pressure diagram. This centroid can be determined by dividing the pressure diagram into regular volumes, which are rectangular or triangular in shape, and then apply the principle of moments to the divided parts.

Since the pressure in a liquid varies uniformly as the depth, h, that is, $p = \gamma h$, the pressure diagram for a submerged plane surface is generally a triangular volume, as shown in Fig. 2-11. The volume of the pressure

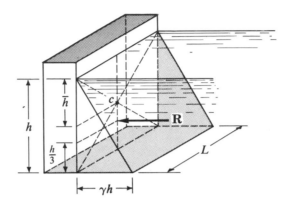

FIGURE 2-11

diagram is

$$\text{Vol.} = \mathbf{R} = \frac{\gamma h(hL)}{2} = \frac{\gamma h a}{2}$$

where hL is the plane surface, or area a, against which the liquid pressure acts. Therefore, the magnitude of the resultant pressure is

$$\mathbf{R} = \gamma \bar{h} a \qquad (2\text{-}9)$$

where $\bar{h}$ is the vertical centroidal distance from the centroid of the area to the liquid surface. This resultant force, $\mathbf{R}$, acts normal to the plane area and passes through the centroid of the pressure diagram.

Example 2-8. The side of a dam has a slope of 12 vertical to 5 horizontal, and retains water to a depth of 18 ft. Determine the horizontal and vertical components of the resultant pressure acting on a one-foot length of the dam using the pressure diagram method.

Solution: Project the sloping surface on a vertical plane, as shown in Fig. 2-12, and draw the pressure diagram for the pressure on this vertical surface. Since the pressure increases with depth, the pressure diagram will be a triangular wedge, 1 ft long. The pressure at the base of the dam will be γh, or $62.4(18) = 1124$ psf. The volume of the wedge that equals the total horizontal component of the pressure is

$$\text{Vol.} = R_h = \frac{1124(18)1}{2} = 10{,}116 \text{ lb/ft of length}$$

which acts through the centroid of the pressure diagram. The centroid is 6 ft above the base of the dam.

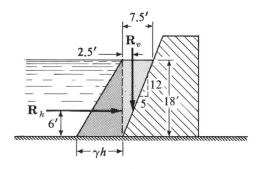

FIGURE 2-12

The vertical component of the pressure is equal to the weight of the water above the sloping surface, or

$$R_v = \frac{62.4(18)7.5(1)}{2} = 4212 \text{ lb/ft of length}$$

and again it acts through the centroid of the vertical pressure volume, or 2.5 ft from the vertical projected area, as shown in Fig. 2-12.

Example 2-9. The tank shown in Fig. 2-13(b) contains water to a depth of 3 ft and oil ($S_g = 0.80$) to a depth of 3 ft. Determine the total pressure exerted by the water and oil on one end of the tank. The tank is 4 ft wide.

Solution: Figure 2-13(a) shows the pressure diagrams produced by the oil and the water. At the junction of the water and the oil, the intensity of pressure is

$$p = \gamma h = 0.80(62.4)3 = 150 \text{ psf.}$$

The volume of the upper triangular pressure diagram is the pressure of the oil on the upper 3 ft of the end of the tank. Thus,

$$R_1 = \frac{150(3)4}{2} = 900 \text{ lb.}$$

This pressure acts 2 ft below the surface of the oil. @ C6 . 7 area

The oil also will produce pressure on the lower 3 ft of the end of the tank, represented by the rectangular pressure diagram. The magnitude of the resultant oil pressure on the lower 3 ft of the tank is

$$R_2 = 150(3)4 = 1800 \text{ lb.}$$

R_2 acts 4.5 ft below the surface of the oil.

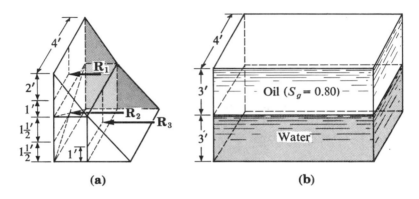

$$(a) \qquad\qquad\qquad\qquad\qquad (b)$$

FIGURE 2-13

The water, occupying the lower 3 ft of the tank, exerts a pressure on the lower 3 ft of the end of the tank forming another triangular pressure diagram. Thus,

$$R_3 = \frac{62.4(3)3(4)}{2} = 1124 \text{ lb.}$$

R_3 acts 5 ft below the surface of the oil.

The total resultant pressure is the sum of the volumes of the pressure diagram, or

$$R = 900 + 1800 + 1124 = 3824 \text{ lb.}$$

The position of the line of action of the resultant pressure can be determined by the principle of moments applied to the force system. Thus,

$$3824 y_R = 900(2) + 1800(4.5) + 1124(5) = 15,520$$

and

$$y_R = \frac{15,520}{3824} = 4.06 \text{ ft,}$$

the distance from the surface of the oil to the resultant force on a vertical line of symmetry.

2-12 FLUID PRESSURE ON PLANE AREAS—FORMULAS

In order to develop formulas for fluid pressure on plane areas, assume the submerged surface in Fig. 2-14 is acted upon by a liquid. The increment of

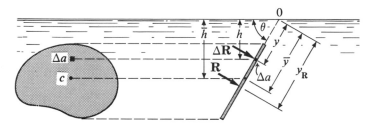

FIGURE 2-14

force $\Delta\mathbf{R}$, acting on any increment of area, Δa, at the vertical distance, h, below the surface of the liquid is

$$\Delta\mathbf{R} = p\,\Delta a = \gamma h\,\Delta a$$

where p is the intensity of the pressure on the increment of area Δa, and h is the vertical distance from the surface of the liquid to that area.

The total force acting on the entire area is

$$\mathbf{R} = \sum \Delta\mathbf{R} = \gamma \sum h\,\Delta a = \gamma \bar{h}a,$$

since $\sum h\,\Delta a$, the first moment of the area, is equal to $\bar{h}a$ as Δa approaches zero.

The product $\gamma\bar{h}$ is the intensity of the pressure at the centroid of the area. Thus, the magnitude of the resultant pressure is equal to the product of the pressure at the centroid and the area of the plane area. This is true in every case for plane areas where the specific weight of the liquid remains constant over that area.

In order to determine the position of the line of action of the resultant pressure, or the center of pressure, the principle of moments applied to a parallel force system is used. Again refer to Fig. 2-14, and take moments with respect to point O on the surface of the liquid,

$$\mathbf{R}y = \sum y \, \Delta \mathbf{R}, \tag{2-10}$$

where $y_\mathbf{R}$ is the moment arm of the resultant pressure. However, $\Delta \mathbf{R} = \gamma h \, \Delta a$, $h = y \sin \theta$, and $\mathbf{R} = \sum \gamma h \, \Delta a$. Therefore, by substituting these values into Eq. (2-10),

$$y_\mathbf{R} \sum \sin \theta \, \Delta a = \sum y \, \gamma y \sin \theta \, \Delta a.$$

By cancelling the constants,

$$y_\mathbf{R} = \frac{\sum y^2 \, \Delta a}{\sum y \, \Delta a}.$$

The term $\sum y^2 \, \Delta a$, as Δa approaches zero, is the second moment of the area and is equal to I_0, and the term $\sum y \, \Delta a$, as Δa approaches zero, is the first moment of the area and is equal to $\bar{y}a$. Therefore,

$$y_\mathbf{R} = \frac{I_0}{\bar{y}a}.$$

A more convenient form of this equation is obtained by transferring the moment of inertia with respect to point O on the surface of the liquid to the horizontal centroidal axis of the area. Since

$$I_0 = I_c + a(\bar{y})^2$$

therefore,

$$y_\mathbf{R} = \frac{I_c + a(\bar{y})^2}{\bar{y}a} = \bar{y} + \frac{I_c}{\bar{y}a}. \tag{2-11}$$

It appears from this equation that the center of pressure is below the centroid of the area by an amount equal to $I_c/a\bar{y}$, measured parallel to the plane area. Also, $y_\mathbf{R}$ is equal to $\bar{y}$ only when the plane area is parallel to the surface of the liquid, or when the plane area is at an infinite depth below the liquid surface.

Example 2-10. Determine completely the resultant hydrostatic pressure acting on one side of a 3-ft-diameter gate. The gate is vertical and its center is 9 ft below the water surface.

Solution: Figure 2-15 shows the gate in the side of a reservoir. The magnitude of the resultant pressure is given by the equation, $\mathbf{R} = \gamma \bar{h} a$. Therefore,

$$\mathbf{R} = 62.4(9) \frac{\pi 3^2}{4} = 3970 \text{ lb.}$$

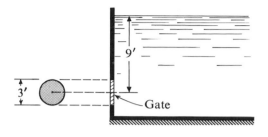

FIGURE 2-15

The center of pressure is determined by the use of Eq. (2-11). Therefore,

$$y_{\mathbf{R}} = 9 + \frac{\pi 3^4 4}{64 \pi 3^2 9} = 9 + \frac{1}{16} = 9.0625 \text{ ft.}$$

Thus, the resultant pressure of 3970 lb acts perpendicular to the gate at a distance of 0.063 ft or 0.75 in. below the center of the gate.

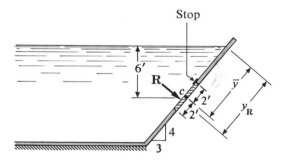

FIGURE 2-16

Example 2-11.   In Fig. 2-16 a reservoir is shown with a 4 ft square gate in the sloping side. The gate is hung on a horizontal shaft through its center. Determine the force on a stop at the top of the gate needed to keep the gate from opening.

Solution: The centroidal distance, $\bar{y}$, is $[5(6)]/4 = 7.5$ ft. The resultant pressure on the gate is

$$\mathbf{R} = \gamma \bar{h} a = 62.4(6)16 = 5990 \text{ lb.}$$

The location of the pressure point is

$$y_{\mathbf{R}} = 7.5 + \frac{4(16)4}{12(16)7.5} = 7.5 + \frac{4}{22.5} = 7.5 + 0.1778.$$

The distance from the shaft to the pressure point measured along the sloping side is 0.1778 ft. Refer to Fig. 2-17. By $\sum M_C = 0$,

$$F(2) = 0.1778(5990) = 1065$$

and

$$F = \frac{1065}{2} = 533 \text{ lb.}$$

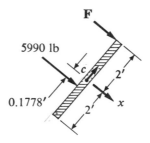

FIGURE 2-17

PROBLEMS

2-29. A 4-ft-diameter vertical gate in the side of a tank has its center 10 ft below the water surface. Determine completely the resultant hydrostatic force acting on the gate.

2-30. If the gate in Prob. 2-29 rotates on a horizontal diametral axis, what moment is required to keep the gate closed?

2-31. A 2-ft-square gate is located in the vertical side of a closed tank. The gate is hinged along a horizontal axis at the upper edge of the gate and water stands to a depth of 9 ft above the hinge, as shown in Fig. P 2-31. The air pressure above the surface of the water is 10 psi.

Determine the magnitude of the horizontal force, **P**, applied at the center of the bottom edge of the gate that will prevent the gate from opening.

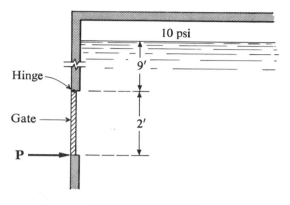

FIGURE P 2-31

2-32. The 2-ft-wide homogeneous rectangular gate of Fig. P 2-32 is located in the side of a tank containing oil ($\gamma = 50$ pcf). A concrete weight, 1 ft square and 1.5 ft long, weighing 150 pcf, holds the gate shut. Determine the maximum height the oil can rise above the center of the gate without allowing the gate to open.

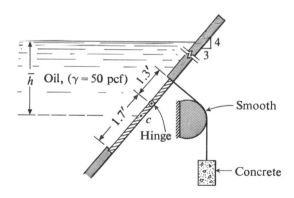

FIGURE P 2-32

2-33. A 5-ft-square gate with two sides horizontal is located in the wall of a tank having a slope of 4 vertical to 3 horizontal. The gate is mounted on a horizontal axis so that it will open automatically when the level of the liquid ($\gamma = 64.0$ pcf) exceeds 10 ft above the center of the gate. Determine the location of the axis with respect to the center of the gate.

2-34. The 3-ft-wide rectangular gate of Fig. P 2-34 is hinged at A. Determine the minimum force, **P**, required to hold the gate closed. The weight of the homogeneous gate is 600 lb and the hinge is smooth.

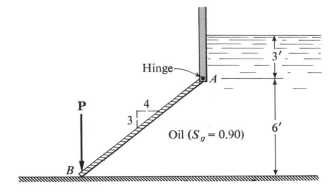

FIGURE P 2-34

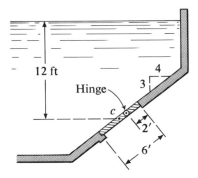

FIGURE P 2-35

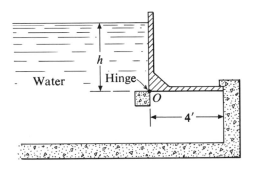

FIGURE P 2-36

2-35. A homogeneous rectangular gate 4 ft wide and 6 ft high is to be mounted on a smooth shaft in the sloping wall of a large tank, as shown in Fig. P 2-35. The gate weighs 5000 lb. Determine the reaction of the smooth stop at the lower edge of the gate when the water level is 12 ft above the center of the gate.

2-36. The gate of Fig. P 2-36 has a uniform width and is considered weightless. It is pinned at O and friction in the hinge may be neglected. For what height, h, will the gate commence to rotate?

2-13 FLUID PRESSURE ON CURVED SURFACES

Often it becomes necessary to evaluate the total pressure exerted by a liquid on a curved surface. To do this, the resultant pressure is determined from its horizontal and vertical components. The horizontal component is evaluated as the force exerted on the projected curved surface on a vertical plane. The vertical component is the weight of the volume of liquid contained vertically above the curved surface and extending to the free surface of the liquid. The vertical component acts through the centroid of the volume of liquid extending from the curved surface vertically to the surface of the liquid.

Note: **The following discussion involves calculus.**

The following examples illustrate the procedure to follow in order to determine the components of the total pressure.

Example 2-12. Determine the total pressure exerted by the water in the tank shown in Fig. 2-18 on the segment of the curved side AB for a 1-ft length of the tank if the equation of the curved surface is $x^2 = y$, where x and y are in feet and the origin is taken at point A.

Solution: For $y = 2$, $x = 2^{1/2} = 1.414$. By Eq. (2-9), $R = \gamma \bar{h} a$,

$$R_h = 62.4(3)2 = 374.4 \text{ lb},$$

and Eq. (2-11), $y_R = \bar{y} + I_c/a\bar{y}$, gives

$$y_R = 3 + \frac{1(8)}{12(2)3} = 3.111 \text{ ft}.$$

The vertical component is equal to the weight of the volume of liquid above the curved surface and extending to the surface of the liquid, or

$$R_v = 62.4(1)\int_0^a da = 62.4 \int_0^{1.414} (4 - y)\, dx = 62.4 \int_0^{1.414} (4\, dx - x^2\, dx)$$

$$R_v = 62.4[4x - (x^3/3)]|_0^{1.414} = 62.4(5.656 - 0.942) = 62.4(4.714)$$
$$= 294.2 \, lb.$$

The centroid of the volume through which the vertical component of the total pressure passes is determined as follows:

$$V\bar{x} = \int_0^{1.414} x \, dv = \int_0^{1.414} x(4 - y) \, dx$$

$$= \int_0^{1.414} x(4 - x^2) \, dx = \int_0^{1.414} (4x - x^3) \, dx$$

$$4.71\bar{x} = [2x^2 - (x^4/4)]|_0^{1.414} = 4 - 1 = 3$$

$$\bar{x} = \frac{3}{4.71} = 0.637 \, ft.$$

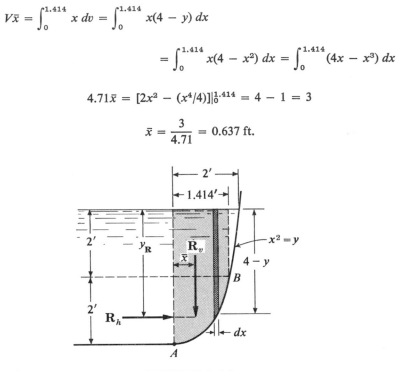

FIGURE 2-18

The magnitude of the resultant total pressure is

$$R = (374.4^2 + 294.2^2)^{1/2} = 476.2 \, lb,$$

which acts as shown in Fig. 2-19.

If the tank shown in Fig. 2-19 were submerged in 4 ft of liquid so that the liquid pressure would act on the outer surface of the segment AB rather than on the inner surface, the resultant pressure would be exactly the same in magnitude and position of line of action but it would be opposite in direction. The following example illustrates the evaluation of the resultant total pressure when the vertical component is upward.

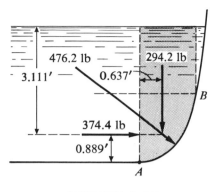

FIGURE 2-19

Example 2-13. Determine the resultant total pressure exerted by the water on the circular gate in Fig. 2-20 per foot of length of the gate.

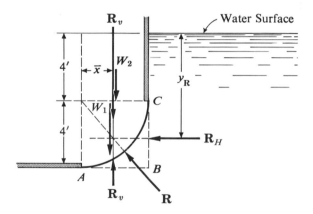

FIGURE 2-20

Solution: First, determine the horizontal component of the total pressure on the projected curved surface on the vertical plane *BC*. The magnitude of the horizontal pressure is given by the equation, $\mathbf{R} = \gamma \bar{h}a$. Therefore,

$$\mathbf{R}_h = 62.4(6)1(4) = 1498 \text{ lb.}$$

Also,

$$y_{\mathbf{R}} = \bar{y} + \frac{I_C}{a\bar{y}} = 6 + \frac{1(64)}{12(4)6} = 6.221 \text{ ft.}$$

Since the vertical component of the total pressure, acting upward, is equal and opposite to the component of the total pressure acting downward when the water is on the opposite side of the gate, the computations will be made for the vertical component, assuming the water to be on the opposite side of the gate with the vertical pressure acting downward. The weight of the water vertically above the curved section and to the left of the curved section is

$$W_1 = \frac{\pi 4^2}{4} (1)62.4 = 784 \text{ lb}$$

and acts at a distance $4r/3\pi$, or $16/9.42 = 1.70$ ft, to the right of point A. The weight of the liquid above the curved section is

$$W_2 = 4(1)4(62.4) = 998 \text{ lb}$$

and acts 2 ft to the right of point A.

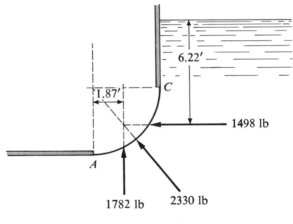

FIGURE 2-21

The total vertical pressure is

$$\mathbf{R}_v = 784 + 998 = 1782 \text{ lb,}$$

and the line of action of this vertical resultant pressure is found as follows:

$$1782\bar{x} = 784(1.7) + 998(2) = 3329$$

$$\bar{x} = \frac{3329}{1782} = 1.87 \text{ ft to the right of point } A.$$

The magnitude of the resultant pressure is the vector sum of the two components, or

$$R = (1498^2 + 1782^2)^{1/2} = 2330 \text{ lb.}$$

Figure 2-21 shows the resultant pressure **R** acting on the gate.

2-14   DAMS

A dam is a structure usually placed across a stream to restrain the flow of water. A gravity dam derives its stability primarily from its weight. As the water builds up on the face of the dam, on the upstream side, it exerts a pressure that tends to cause the dam to slide or overturn. Within the structure compressive and shearing stresses are produced. The maximum frictional force possible between the dam and the supporting foundation is

$$F' = \mu N$$

where   N is the upward reaction of the foundation against the dam, and μ is the coefficient of friction.

The ratio of the maximum frictional force possible to the actual frictional force required to hold the dam from sliding gives the factor of safety against sliding, or

$$\text{F.S.(sliding)} = \frac{F'}{F} = \frac{\mu N}{F}.$$

Some forces on the dam produce overturning moments with respect to the toe of the dam (see Fig. 2-22) and others produce resisting moments. *The ratio of the resisting moments to the overturning moments is the factor of safety against overturning*, or

$$\text{F.S.(overturning)} = \frac{\text{Resisting Moments}}{\text{Overturning Moments}}.$$

Where the soil or foundation beneath the dam is somewhat porous, water will seep under the dam, thereby producing an uplift force that must be considered in determining the total overturning moment. Figure 2-22 is a free-body diagram of a 1-ft section of a concrete gravity dam for which the uplift force varies from the full hydrostatic pressure at the heel to zero at the toe. Generally, it is desirable in the design of dams to have the resultant of the forces act at the middle third of any horizontal section taken through the dam in order to eliminate tensile stresses in the concrete.

In Fig. 2-22, forces W_1 and W_2 resist the overturning moments produced by forces R and U, where U is the uplift force.

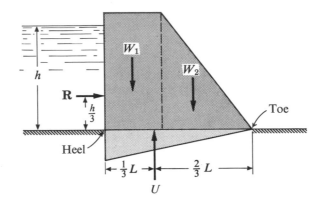

FIGURE 2-22

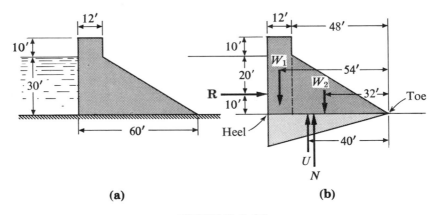

                  (a)   **(b)**

FIGURE 2-23

Example 2-14. Determine the factor of safety with respect to sliding and overturning for the concrete dam shown in Fig. 2-23, if the coefficient of friction between the base and the dam is 0.40 and the uplift force varies from full hydrostatic pressure at the heel to zero at the toe.

Solution: A free-body diagram of the dam is shown in Fig. 2-23(b). A 1-ft length of the dam is used. The horizontal pressure exerted by the water on the dam is

$$R = \gamma \bar{h} a = 62.4(15)30(1) = 28{,}100 \text{ lb.}$$

The uplift force is

$$U = \frac{\gamma h a}{2} = \frac{62.4(30)60}{2} = 56,200 \text{ lb.}$$

The weight of the dam is computed at 150 lb/cu ft of concrete:

$$W_1 = 12(1)40(150) = 72,000 \text{ lb,}$$

$$W_2 = \frac{48(1)30(150)}{2} = 108,000 \text{ lb.}$$

The factor of safety with respect to sliding is computed as follows: By $\sum F_x = 0$,

$$F = R = 28,100 \text{ lb,}$$

which is the actual frictional force existing at the base of the dam.

The maximum frictional force possible between the dam and the foundation is $F' = \mu N$. Solving for N,

$$N = 72,000 + 108,000 - 56,200 = 123,800 \text{ lb.}$$

Therefore,

$$F' = 0.40(123,800) = 49,520 \text{ lb,}$$

and

$$\text{F.S.(sliding)} = \frac{49,520}{28,100} = 1.76.$$

Since the factor of safety with respect to overturning is the resisting moment divided by the overturning moment, where the moments of the forces are taken with respect to the toe of the dam,

$$\text{F.S.(overturning)} = \frac{72,000(54) + 108,000(32)}{28,000(10) + 56,200(40)} = \frac{7,344,000}{2,529,000} = 2.90.$$

Example 2-15. Determine the factor of safety with respect to overturning for the sea wall shown in Fig. 2-24(a). Assume that uplift varies from full hydrostatic pressure at the heel to zero at the toe.

Solution: A 1-ft length of the sea wall will be used. The free-body diagram of
the sea wall is shown in Fig. 2-24(b).

$$\mathbf{R}_h = \gamma \bar{h} a = 62.4(6)12 = 4{,}493 \text{ lb}$$

$$\mathbf{R}_v = \frac{12(12)1(62.4)}{2} = 4{,}493 \text{ lb}$$

$$\mathbf{W}_1 = \mathbf{W}_2 = \frac{15(15)1(150)}{2} = 16{,}875 \text{ lb}$$

$$\mathbf{W}_3 = 6(15)1(150) = 13{,}500 \text{ lb}$$

$$\mathbf{U} = \frac{12(62.4)36}{2} = 13{,}500 \text{ lb}$$

$$\text{F.S.} = \frac{4493(32) + 16{,}875(26) + 13{,}500(18) + 16{,}875(10)}{4493(4) + 13{,}500(24)}$$

$$\text{F.S.} = \frac{143{,}800 + 438{,}000 + 243{,}000 + 168{,}750}{17{,}972 + 324{,}000} = \frac{993{,}550}{341{,}972} = 2.91.$$

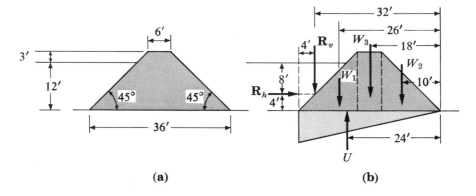

(a)   (b)

FIGURE 2-24

PROBLEMS

2-37. The curved surface *AB* in Fig. P 2-37 is the quadrant of a circular
cylinder and is 6 ft long. Determine the magnitude of the horizontal and
vertical components of the resultant hydrostatic pressure on the curved
surface due to the water in the tank when
(a) $r = 8$ ft and $z = 0$ ft.
(b) $r = 10$ ft and $z = 4$ ft.
(c) $r = 12$ ft and $z = 6$ ft.
(d) $r = 4$ ft and $z = 20$ ft.

2-38. The curved gate *AB* in Fig. P 2-38 is the quadrant of a circular cylinder hinged at *A* and resting against a smooth wall at *B*. The gate is 4 ft long. Determine the horizontal and vertical components of the reaction at *A* and *B*.

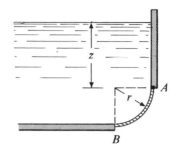

FIGURE P 2-37

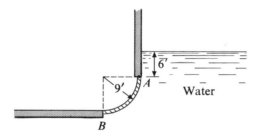

FIGURE P 2-38

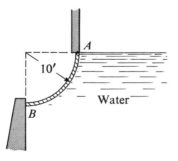

FIGURE P 2-39

2-39. The curved gate *AB*, shown in Fig. P 2-39, is the quadrant of a circular cylinder. It is hinged at *A* and rests against the smooth wall at *B*. The gate is 12 ft long. Determine the horizontal and vertical components of the reaction at A and B due to the hydrostatic pressure, assuming the gate is weightless.

2-40. A gate, 4 ft long, in the shape of a quadrant of a cylinder, is hinged along the top, as shown in Fig. P 2-40. Determine the components of the reaction of the hinge at point A, and the force, F, necessary to hold the gate in a closed position. Neglect its weight.

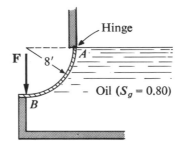

FIGURE P 2-40

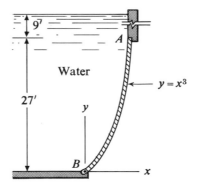

FIGURE P 2-41

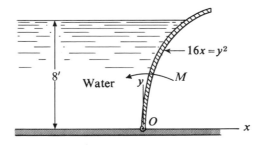

FIGURE P 2-42

2-41. Determine the horizontal reaction at the notch A on the gate AB, which is hinged at B. The tank contains water, and is 6 ft long.

2-42. Determine the moment about the hinge at O necessary to hold the curved gate in Fig. P 2-42 in the position shown. The gate is 8 ft long.

2-43. A tank car, 8 ft in diameter, is filled with fuel oil ($\gamma = 56.9$ pcf). Determine the resultant force per foot of length along the car that is exerted by the oil on the curved surface of a vertical half of the tank car.

2-44. Determine the minimum allowable thickness of a 24-in.-diameter steel pipe that carries fluid under a pressure of 150 psi. Assume a working stress in the pipe of 12,000 psi.

2-45. Figure P 2-45 shows the cross section of a concrete wall ($\gamma = 150$ pcf). Assume that the uplift varies uniformly from full hydrostatic pressure at the heel to zero at the toe. Determine the factor of safety with respect to overturning.

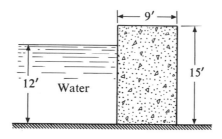

FIGURE P 2-45

2-46. The gravity dam of Fig. P 2-45 is made of concrete ($\gamma = 150$ pcf.) Seepage pressure varies linearly from a full head at the heel to zero at the toe of the dam. Determine
(a) the factor of safety with respect to overturning, and
(b) the minimum permissible coefficient of friction between the dam and the foundation if a factor of safety with respect to sliding of 2.0 is to be maintained.

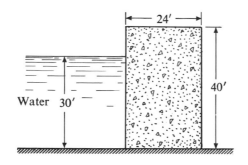

FIGURE P 2-46

2-47. The gravity dam of Fig. P 2-47 is made of concrete (γ = 150 pcf). Pressure due to seepage under the dam varies linearly from a full hydrostatic head at the heel to zero at the toe of the dam.

  (a) Determine the factor of safety with respect to overturning.

  (b) If the coefficient of friction between the dam and the foundation is 0.50, determine the factor of safety with respect to sliding.

2-48. Figure P 2-48 shows the cross section of a concrete dam (γ = 150 pcf). Assume that the uplift varies uniformly from full hydrostatic pressure

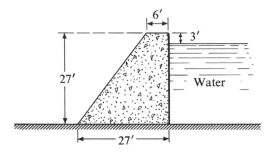

FIGURE P 2-47

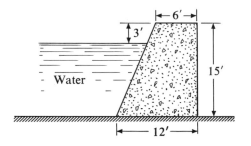

FIGURE P 2-48

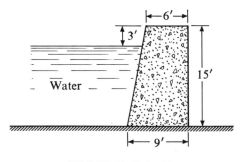

FIGURE P 2-49

at the heel to zero at the toe. Determine the overturning moment per foot of length of the dam.

2-49. The gravity dam of Fig. P 2-49 is made of concrete ($\gamma = 150$ pcf). Assume no uplift due to seepage. Determine

    (a) the factor of safety with respect to overturning, and

    (b) the factor of safety with respect to sliding if the coefficient of friction between the dam and the foundation is 0.50.

2-50. Figure P 2-50 shows the cross section of a concrete gravity dam that weighs 150 pcf. Assume that the uplift pressure varies uniformly from full hydrostatic pressure at the heel to zero at the toe. Determine the minimum coefficient of friction between the dam and the foundation required to prevent sliding for the depth of water shown.

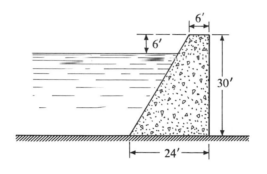

FIGURE P 2-50

2-51. A gravity wall shown in Fig. P 2-51, weighing 150 pcf, is subjected to an uplift pressure varying uniformly from full hydrostatic pressure at the heel to zero at the toe. Determine the maximum depth of water that may be maintained on the face of the wall without reducing the factor with respect to failure by overturning below 1.80.

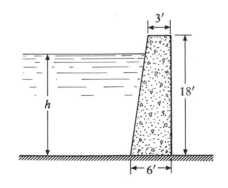

FIGURE P 2-51

Chapter 3

Buoyancy

3-1 INTRODUCTION

The fact that wood floats and that bodies immersed in a liquid weigh less
than in air are phenomena related to the buoyant forces that act on these
bodies. *The bouyant force is defined as the resultant of the total upward and
downward pressures exerted by a fluid on a body, submerged or partially*

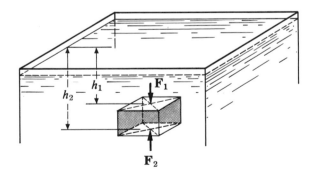

FIGURE 3-1

submerged in that fluid. Refer to Fig. 3-1. The buoyant force, acting on the submerged body, is equal to $\mathbf{F}_2 - \mathbf{F}_1$, where $\mathbf{F}_2$ is the total pressure exerted upward by the fluid on the body, and $\mathbf{F}_1$ is the total pressure exerted downward by the fluid on the body.

3-2 MAGNITUDE OF BUOYANT FORCE

The magnitude of the buoyant force, acting on a body submerged or partially submerged in a fluid, is equal to the weight of the fluid displaced by the body. This statement is known as Archimedes' principle. For example, let body A in Fig. 3-2 be submerged in a liquid that has a specific weight of

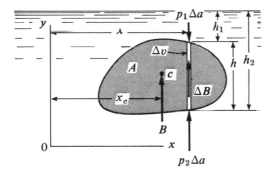

FIGURE 3-2

γ lb/cu ft. Divide this body into differential vertical elements of volume. Each element has a cross-sectional area, Δa. The total pressure of the liquid acting downward on the element ΔV, shown in Fig. 3-2, is

$$p_1 \Delta a = \gamma h_1 \Delta a$$

and the total pressure of the liquid acting upward is

$$p_2 \Delta a = \gamma h_2 \Delta a.$$

The resultant buoyant force, $\Delta \mathbf{B}$, acting on this element, is

$$\Delta \mathbf{B} = \gamma h_2 \Delta a - \gamma h_1 \Delta a = \gamma \Delta a(h_2 - h_1).$$

But,

$$h_2 - h_1 = h, \quad \text{and} \quad h \Delta a = \Delta V.$$

Therefore,

$$\mathbf{B} = \gamma \sum \Delta V,$$

and, as ΔV approaches 0,

$$\mathbf{B} = \gamma V$$

where γ = the specific weight of the fluid, and
           V = the volume of the submerged body.

The term γV is the weight of the volume of the fluid that is displaced by the body.

3-3   ACTION LINE OF BUOYANT FORCE

The differential buoyant forces acting on the differential vertical elements of volume of the body in Fig. 3-2 constitute a parallel system of forces. The location of the line of action of the resultant buoyant force can be deter-

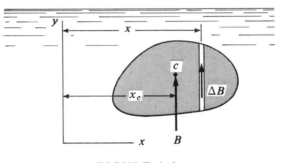

FIGURE 3-3

mined by applying the principle of moments to this force system. Thus, referring to Fig. 3-3,

$$\mathbf{B}x_c = \sum x \,\Delta\mathbf{B} = \gamma \sum x \,\Delta V$$

where x_c is the distance from a coordinate axis to the position of the line of action of the resultant buoyant force. But $\mathbf{B} = \gamma V$, and the summation of $x \,\Delta V$, as ΔV approaches zero, equals $\bar{x}V$, where $\bar{x}$ is the centroidal distance from the coordinate axis to the centroid of the volume. Thus,

$$\gamma V x_c = \gamma \bar{x} V$$

and, by cancellation,

$$x_c = \bar{x},$$

which proves that the resultant buoyant force acts through the centroid of the submerged volume, or through the centroid of the volume of the fluid displaced by the body.

3-4 APPLICATION

A body, partially or completely submerged, will remain in equilibrium as long as the buoyant force is equal to the weight of the body and these forces are equal, opposite, and collinear. When the weight of the body is greater than the weight of the fluid displaced by the body, it will sink; when the weight of the body is less, it will float at a level where the weight of the displaced fluid equals the weight of the body.

Since the specific gravity of a solid is equal to the weight of the solid divided by the weight of an equal volume of water, the buoyant force provides a convenient factor in this determination. Since the buoyant force represents the weight of an equal volume of water, the specific gravity of a substance may be computed as follows:

$$\text{Specific gravity} = \frac{\text{weight of substance in air}}{\text{wt. in air} - \text{wt. in water}} = \frac{\text{wt. in air}}{\text{buoyant force}}.$$

The stability of floating objects such as ships, scows, and barges is dependent on the turning moment produced by the couple formed by the resultant weight and the resultant buoyant force. For stable equilibrium, these two forces must remain equal, opposite, and collinear, or they must tend to produce this condition when temporarily displaced from a collinear position. For example, Fig. 3-4(a) indicates a barge that is being tipped slightly due to wave or wind action. The centroid of the weight of the barge is at G and the centroid of the displaced fluid or buoyant force is at b. The couple $\mathbf{W}d$ or $\mathbf{B}d$ tends to right the tipped barge, which will bring the forces back to stable equilibrium, as shown in Fig. 3-4(b).

If the rectangular body rests in the liquid, as shown in Fig. 3-5(a), it remains stable as long as the buoyant and weight forces are equal, opposite, and collinear. However, if the body is tipped slightly, the couple developed will not tend to bring it back to stable equilibrium in the same position but will tend to complete the tipping process due to the couple $\mathbf{W}d$ or $\mathbf{B}d$, which is clockwise, until the body becomes stable, as shown in Fig. 3-5(c).

The point M, where the line of action of the buoyant force intersects the vertical axis of symmetry of the body, is called the metacenter. If the metacenter is above the center of gravity, the body will return to its original position when tipped, but if the metacenter is below the center of gravity, the body will tend to overturn when tipped slightly. (In Fig. 3-4, the metacenter is above the center of gravity.) This is a matter of great importance in the design of boats and ships.

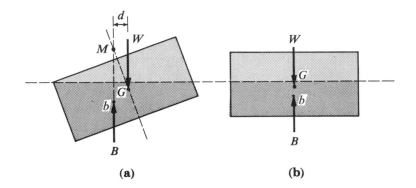

FIGURE 3-4

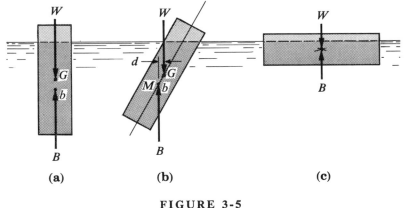

FIGURE 3-5

Example 3-1. Determine the buoyant force developed on a 4-ft-diameter. sphere that is completely submerged in salt water ($\gamma = 66$ pcf).

Solution: Since the buoyant force is the product of the specific weight of the salt water and the volume of the sphere or the volume of the salt water displaced by the sphere,

$$\mathbf{B} = \gamma V = \frac{66(4\pi 2^3)}{3} = 2210 \text{ lb.}$$

Example 3-2. A sample of material weighs 800 grams in air and 500 grams when suspended in water. Determine the specific gravity and the density of the material.

Solution: The weight of the displaced fluid is the buoyant force. Thus

$$B = 800 - 500 = 300 \text{ gm,}$$

which, also, is the weight of the water displaced. Since the specific gravity is the weight of a material divided by the weight of an equal volume of water,

$$S_g = \frac{800}{300} = 2.67.$$

Also, since the density of a material is w/g,

$$\rho = \frac{2.67(62.4)}{32.2} = 5.17 \text{ slugs/cu ft.}$$

(Note: For problems in this text, the specific weight of water will be assumed at 62.4 pcf when the temperature is not given.)

PROBLEMS

3-1.   A body, which has a volume of 4 cu ft, is immersed in water and a force of 40 lb is required to keep it immersed. When it is immersed in an unknown liquid, a force of 25 lb is required to keep it immersed. Determine the specific gravity of the unknown liquid.

3-2.   A block, which has a volume of 2 cu ft, is immersed in oil ($S_g = 0.80$), and a force of 20 lb is required to keep it immersed. Determine the specific weight of the block.

3-3.   Determine the specific gravity of a piece of metal that weighs 7.50 lb when immersed in an oil ($S_g = 0.80$), and 6 lb when immersed in water.

3-4.   A force of 25 lb is required to keep a 4-cu-ft block immersed in oil ($S_g = 0.85$), and a force of 50 lb is required to keep it immersed in another liquid. Determine the density of this other liquid.

3-5.   A block, which has a volume of 4 cu ft, is completely immersed in water by a force of 75 lb. Determine the density of the block.

3-6.   A quantity of gravel, which weighs 1000 grams in air, weighs 625 grams when completely immersed in water. Determine the specific weight of the gravel.

3-7.   A quantity of gravel weighs 40 lb in air, and 25 lb when suspended in water. Determine the specific gravity of the gravel.

3-8.   The homogeneous timber, *AB*, of Fig. P 3-8, is 6 in. by 12 in. in cross section. Determine the specific weight of the timber and the tension in the rope.

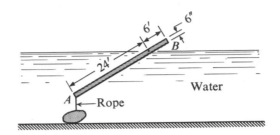

FIGURE P 3-8

3-9.   Determine the number of logs ($\gamma = 34$ pcf) needed to form a raft that will be used to transport 200 symmetrically placed sacks of portland cement across a lake. The logs are 15 ft long and have an average diameter of 12 in. Portland cement weighs 94 lb/sack and the floor supporting the cement weighs 220 lb. Assume that only the logs will be submerged.

3-10. A 1-ft thick homogeneous block of wood ($S_g = 0.60$) is submerged in oil ($S_g = 0.80$) and loaded as indicated in Fig. P 3-10. Determine the total force, **P**, required to hold the block in the position shown.

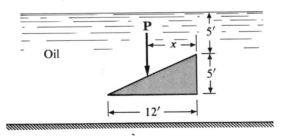

FIGURE P 3-10

3-11. Determine the total force that is required to hold the wooden block ($\gamma = 40$ pcf), which is partially submerged in water in the position shown in Fig. P 3-11, in equilibrium. The block is 2 ft thick.

3-12. The hollow, thin-walled float of Fig. P 3-12 is held in a vertical position by 2 cu ft of concrete ($\gamma = 150$ pcf). If the volume of concrete is doubled, determine the distance from the top of the float to the water's surface. The float is open at the bottom and weighs 200 lb.

3-13. A thin-walled tank of Fig. P 3-13 is 10 ft long and closed at one end. It has a cross-sectional area of 4 sq ft and weighs 200 lb. The open end of the tank is lowered into the water until only 2 ft of the tank projects above the water's surface. The tank is held in this position by a sus-

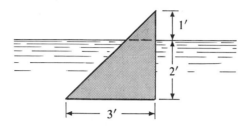

FIGURE P 3-11

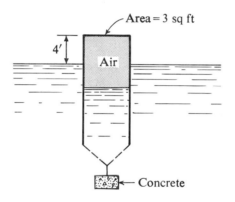

FIGURE P 3-12

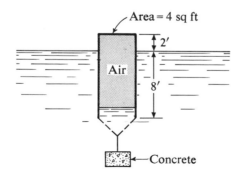

FIGURE P 3-13

pended block of concrete (γ = 150 pcf). Determine the volume of the concrete block.

3-14. The circular gate of Fig. P 3-14 is located in the sloping side of a wall and is mounted on a horizontal shaft. A concrete block (γ = 150 pcf), immersed in oil (S_g = 0.80), is attached to the gate by a flexible cable as shown. Determine the volume of concrete required to hold the gate in the position shown if there are no stops for the gate.

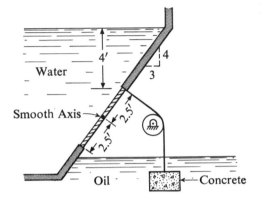

FIGURE P 3-14

Chapter *4*

Steady Flow of Liquids— Closed Conduits

4-1 INTRODUCTION

A fluid is composed of an infinite number of particles. As the fluid moves or flows in a pipe, the particles may move in a definite pattern or they may move in an unpredictable pattern, each particle moving in different directions with velocities changing constantly. *Where fluids move in a definite pattern with the streamlines parallel to the sides of the pipes, the motion is referred to as laminar flow. Where laminar flow does not exist the flow is turbulent; the particles move in various directions at varying speeds.* In both types of flow, the fluid directly adjacent to the sides of the pipe remains stationary, forming a fluid coating on the inner surface of the pipe. The fluid at the center of the pipe generally has the greatest velocity. The variation of the velocity in the direction of flow of a fluid for laminar and turbulent flow is shown in Fig. 4-1. The average of all the resultants of particle velocities represents the velocity of the fluid in the direction of flow in the pipe.

Experiments have shown that if the flow in a pipe is laminar and the velocity is gradually increased, it will abruptly change to turbulent flow. The velocity at which this change occurs is known as the *upper critical velocity*. Conversely, if the flow is turbulent and the velocity is gradually decreased, the flow will become laminar at a velocity lower than the upper critical velocity. This reduced velocity is called the *lower critical velocity*. The critical velocity depends on the viscosity and density of the fluid, the diameter of the pipe, and the initial turbulence that is produced at the pipe entrance.

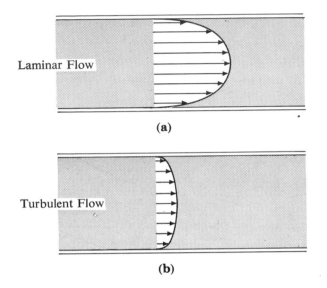

(a)

(b)

FIGURE 4-1

4-2 CONTINUITY OF FLOW

When the mass of fluid passing any section of a pipe remains constant over a period of time, the flow is called steady flow. When the mass of fluid passing every section of a pipe is the same, "*continuity of flow*" occurs. That is,

$$\rho_1 a_1 v_1 = \rho_2 a_2 v_2 = \text{a constant},$$

where ρ(rho) = the density of the fluid, mass/unit volume
a = the cross-sectional area of fluid flowing in the pipe, ft^2
v = the average velocity of the fluid at any section of the pipe, ft/sec.

For liquids, for which the density is assumed to be constant, the equation of continuity becomes,

$$a_1 v_1 = a_2 v_2 = \text{a constant},$$

where av represents the discharge of the fluid across any section of the pipe; a is in square feet and v is in feet/second; av is in cubic feet/second. Substituting Q for av, the equation of continuity, assuming constant density, becomes,

$$Q_1 = Q_2 = \text{a constant.}$$

Example 4-1. A 6 in by 3-in.-diameter reducer connects a 6 in. and a 3 in. water line. If the discharge in the line is 0.314 cfs, determine the velocity in (a) the 6 in. line, and (b) the 3 in. line.

Solution: Since $Q = a_1 v_1 = a_2 v_2$,

therefore

$$0.314 = \frac{\pi}{16} v_1$$

and

$$v_1 = \frac{16}{\pi} (0.314) = 1.6 \text{ fps in the 6-in. line.}$$

Also,

$$0.314 = \frac{\pi}{64} v_2$$

and

$$v_2 = \frac{64}{\pi} (0.314) = 6.4 \text{ fps in the 3-in. line.}$$

From the example above, it will be noted that

$$\frac{v_1}{v_2} = \frac{d_2^2}{d_1^2} = \frac{3^2}{6^2} = \frac{9}{36} = \frac{1}{4}.$$

Also,

$$\frac{v_1}{v_2} = \frac{a_2}{a_1}.$$

Thus, where continuity of flow occurs in two pipes of different cross-sectional areas, the velocities will vary inversely as the areas, or inversely as the square of the diameters.

Example 4-2. A 6-in.-diameter pipe is to discharge 1,000,000 gallons of water/day (mgd). Determine the velocity required.

Solution: One cubic foot of water is equivalent to 7.48 gallons. Therefore,

$$\frac{1,000,000}{7.48} = 133,700 \text{ cubic feet of water/day,}$$

and

$$\frac{133,700}{24(60)60} = 1.547 \text{ cfs} = Q.$$

Therefore,

$$v = \frac{Q}{a} = \frac{1.547(16)}{\pi} = 7.88 \text{ fps.}$$

4-3   THE BERNOULLI EQUATION

In order to arrive at an equation of flow in a closed conduit, the velocity of the flow at any point in the pipe is assumed to be constant (steady flow). The equation of flow then is derived by applying Newton's second law of motion, $\sum \mathbf{F} = Ma$, to a differential mass of fluid forming a streamline.

Note: The following disscussion involves calculus.

The direction of motion is assumed at an angle θ with the horizontal, as shown in Fig. 4-2. The frictional forces $\mathbf{F}_1$, $\mathbf{F}_2$, $\mathbf{F}_3$, and $\mathbf{F}_4$ act opposite

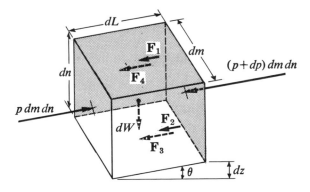

FIGURE 4-2

to the direction of flow and may be replaced by a resultant frictional force $\mathbf{F}_s$. Substituting the forces of Fig. 4-2 into the equation $\sum \mathbf{F}_L = Ma$, gives,

$$p \, dm \, dn - (p + dp) \, dm \, dn - dW \sin \theta - \mathbf{F}_s = dMa.$$

Now, substituting dW/g for dM and dv/dt for a, and cancelling terms, gives,

$$-dp \, dm \, dn - dW \sin \theta - \mathbf{F}_s = \frac{dW}{g} \frac{dv}{dt}.$$

Now, replace dW by $\gamma \, dL \, dm \, dn$ and dL/dt by v. The result is,

$$-dp \, dm \, dn - \gamma \, dm \, dn \, dL \sin \theta - \mathbf{F}_s = \frac{\gamma}{g} dm \, dn \, v \, dv.$$

Divide by $\gamma \, dm \, dn$ and replace $dL \sin \theta$ by dz. The result is,

$$-\int_{p_1}^{p_z} \frac{dp}{\gamma} - \int_{z_1}^{z_2} dz - \int_{L_1}^{L_2} \frac{\mathbf{F}_s}{\gamma \, dm \, dn} = \int_{v_1}^{v_2} \frac{v \, dv}{g}. \qquad (4\text{-}1)$$

In this equation, γ is assumed to be a constant. By substituting h_f for $\int_{L_1}^{L_2} \mathbf{F}_s/(\gamma \, dm \, dn)$, and integrating Eq. (4-1), we get

$$-\frac{p_2}{\gamma} + \frac{p_1}{\gamma} - z_2 + z_1 - h_f = \frac{v_2^2 - v_1^2}{2g}.$$

The resulting equation is

$$\frac{p_1}{\gamma} + z_1 + \frac{v_1^2}{2g} = \frac{p_2}{\gamma} + z_2 + \frac{v_2^2}{2g} + h_f, \qquad (4\text{-}2)$$

which is known as the modified Bernoulli equation.

Each of the terms in Eq. (4-2) represents feet of fluid flowing. The term p_1/γ is the pressure head at section 1 of a pipe and its units are in feet since the units of p/γ are lb/ft^2 × ft^3/lb = ft. The term z is the vertical distance of the section above a datum, or reference plane. This distance is expressed in feet. The velocity head may be expressed in the units ft^2/sec^2 × sec^2/ft = ft.

The sum, $p_1/\gamma + z_1 + v_1^2/2g$, represents the total head at section 1 and the sum, $p_2/\gamma + z_2 + v_2^2/2g$, represents the total head at section 2. Both sums are expressed in feet of fluid flowing. The difference between these total heads is the loss of head, h_f, which occurs in the stream as it flows from section 1 to section 2, due to pipe friction. It is also expressed in feet of fluid flowing.

Unless otherwise stated, the diameters of pipes that are given in the following examples and problems are assumed to be the exact internal diameters of the pipes. Actual diameters of various pipes are given in Appendix A.

Example 4-3. At section A in a 6-in.-diameter pipe, carrying oil ($S_g = 0.85$), the pressure is 12 psig. At section B, 20 ft above section A in the direction of flow, the diameter of the pipe is 16 in. The flow in the pipe is 3.14 cfs. Determine the pressure at section B if the head loss between sections A and B is 6 ft of oil.

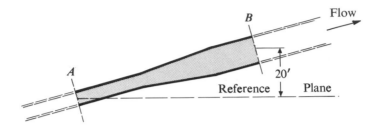

FIGURE 4-3

Solution: Figure 4-3 is a sketch of the pipe system. The reference plane is taken through the center of the 6-in. pipe at section A. By writing the Bernoulli equation for the length of pipe between sections A and B, the pressure at section B can be found. The average velocity at section A is

$$v_A = \frac{Q}{a} = \frac{3.14(16)}{\pi} = 16 \text{ fps.}$$

Since the average velocity at section B is inversely proportional to the square of the diameters,

$$\frac{v_B}{16} = \frac{36}{16^2}; \qquad v_B = \frac{36(16)}{16(16)} = 2.25 \text{ fps}$$

or

$$v_B = \frac{Q}{a} = \frac{3.14(9)4}{3.14(16)} = 2.25 \text{ fps.}$$

Substituting these values into the Bernoulli equation gives,

$$\frac{12}{0.433(0.85)} + 0 + \frac{16^2}{64.4} = \frac{p_B}{0.433(0.85)} + 20 + \frac{2.25^2}{64.4} + 6.0$$

$$\frac{p_B}{0.433(0.85)} = 32.61 + 3.97 - 20.0 - 0.08 - 6.0 = 10.50.$$

Therefore,

$$p_B = 0.368(10.50) = 3.86 \text{ psig.}$$

PROBLEMS

4-1. By what number should the discharge in gpm be multiplied to convert it to cfs?

4-2. A 6-in.-diameter pipe line is carrying 300 gpm. Determine the average velocity of the liquid in the pipe in fps.

4-3. A 6-in.-diameter pipe is carrying gasoline ($S_g = 0.65$) with an average velocity of 10 fps. Determine the discharge in (a) slugs/sec, (b) gpm, and (c) cfs.

4-4. Convert a flow of 1 mgd to cfs.

4-5. What minimum diameter pipe is required to discharge 600 gpm with a maximum average velocity of 8 fps?

4-6. A 4-in.-diameter pipe carries 200 gpm of water under a pressure of 36 psig. Determine (a) the pressure head in ft of water, (b) the velocity head, and (c) the total head. The reference plane is 10 ft below the center of the pipe.

4-7. A 2-in.-diameter pipe discharges into a 6-in.-diameter pipe; both are flowing full. Determine the velocity head in each pipe when they are carrying 400 gpm of oil.

4-8. At section A in a 6-in.-diameter pipe, which is carrying 3.14 cfs of water, the pressure is 8 psig. Fifteen ft below section A, at section B, as shown in Fig. P 4-8, the diameter of the pipe is 12 in. and the pressure is 10 psig. Determine the direction of flow and the head loss between sections A and B.

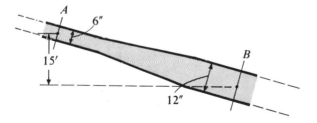

FIGURE P 4-8

4-9. The diameter of pipe changes from 6 in. at point A, to 16 in. at point B, as shown in Fig. P 4-9. Point A is 18 ft below point B. The pressure at A is 10 psig and the pressure at B is 4 psig. If the discharge is 4 cfs of water, determine the direction of flow and the frictional loss between points A and B.

4-10. A horizontal pipe carrying gasoline ($S_g = 0.65$) changes in diameter from 2 in. to 4 in. in the direction of flow. If the gage pressure at the 2-in. section is 12 psi when the discharge is 0.78 cfs, and the friction loss is 6 ft of gasoline, determine the pressure in the 4-in.-diameter pipe.

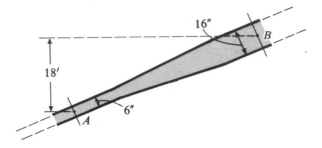

FIGURE P 4-9

4-11. Kerosene ($\gamma = 50.6$ pcf) flows from a horizontal 6-in.-diameter pipe, in which the pressure is 10 psig, into a horizontal 12-in.-diameter pipe, in which the pressure is 24 psig. Determine the discharge if the frictional head loss is 8 ft of kerosene.

4-12. A 12-in.-diameter pipe carries 5.23 cfs of oil ($S_g = 0.90$) through a horizontal 90° reducing bend to an 8-in.-diameter pipe, as shown in Fig. P 4-12. If the pressure at the 12-in. section is 6 psig and the frictional head loss for the bend is 3 ft of oil, determine the pressure at the 8-in. section.

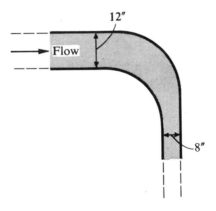

FIGURE P 4-12

4-13. A 4-in.-diameter pipe, connected to a standpipe, discharges water into the air 110 ft below the water level in the standpipe, as shown in Fig. P 4-13. Determine the discharge if the total frictional head loss between the water level and the discharge end of the 4-in. pipe is 12 ft of water.

4-14. A horizontal pipe tapers gradually from a 6-in.-diameter to a 2-in.-diameter pipe in the direction of flow. Neglect friction. Determine the

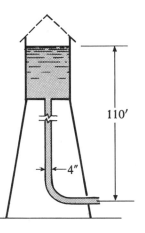

FIGURE P 4-13

difference between the pressures in the two pipe sizes when the discharge is 1.57 cfs of fuel oil at 70°F.

4-15. At point A in a pipe line carrying 15 cfs of crude oil ($\gamma = 57.8$ pcf), the diameter is 12 in. and the pressure is 30 psig. At point B, 15 ft lower, in the same line, the diameter is 18 in., as shown in Fig. P 4-15. If the flow is from A to B, and the frictional head loss between the two points is 10 ft of oil, determine the pressure at point B.

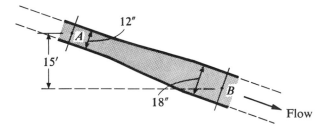

FIGURE P 4-15

4-16. Water flows from a reservoir through a 6-in.-diameter pipe, 1200 ft long, and discharges into the open air, as shown in Fig. P 4-16. If the discharge end of the pipe is 50 ft below the water level in the reservoir and the frictional head loss is 0.04 ft of water per ft of pipe, determine the discharge. Neglect the loss of head at the entrance to the pipe.

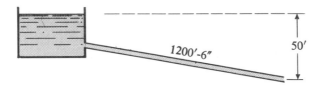

FIGURE P 4-16

4-17.   A horizontal pipe, carrying crude oil ($S_g = 0.83$) changes in diameter from 6 in. to 3 in. in the direction of flow. If the pressure at the 6-in. portion is 10 psi when the discharge is 1.0 cfs, determine the pressure at the 3-in. section. Neglect friction.

4-18.   A large, closed tank contains gasoline ($S_g = 0.675$). A hose leads from the bottom of the tank to a point 25 ft above the level of the gasoline in the tank, as shown in Fig. P 4-18. The diameter of the jet of gasoline,

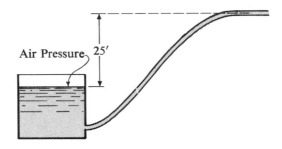

FIGURE P 4-18

where the hose discharges into the air, is 2.5 in. The frictional head loss in the hose is 18 ft of gasoline. Determine the air pressure that must be maintained above the surface of the gasoline in the tank in order to produce a discharge of 0.785 cfs.

4-19.   A 12-in.-diameter pipe is connected to a 6-in. pipe by a horizontal reducer, as shown in Fig. P 4-19. The pressure at A is 20 psig when the

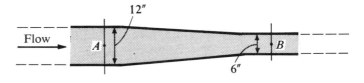

FIGURE P 4-19

discharge is 1.2 cfs, flowing from A to B, and the loss of pressure between A and B due to friction is 3 psig. Determine the pressure at point B if the liquid is (a) water, and (b) oil ($S_g = 0.85$).

4-20. In Fig. P 4-20, with 0.52 cfs of water flowing from A to B, the pressure at A is 12 psig and at B the pressure is 9 psig. Determine the head loss between A and B.

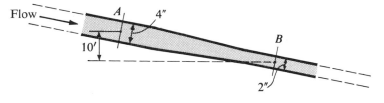

FIGURE P 4-20

4-4 ENERGY CONCEPT

Although each term in the Bernoulli equation is generally expressed in feet of fluid flowing, each term also expresses the energy involved per unit weight of fluid flowing. *The kinetic energy* due to the velocity of one pound of fluid, expressed as $\frac{1}{2}Mv^2$, is

$$\frac{1}{2}Mv^2 = \frac{\frac{1}{2}(1)v^2}{g} = \frac{v^2}{2g},$$

which is the velocity head in the Bernoulli equation. *The elevation head* represents the *potential energy* per pound of the fluid due to its elevation above some reference plane. As an elevation, it is indicated in feet, but as energy per pound of fluid, it can be expressed as foot-pounds/pound. The same generalization applies to the last term, p/γ, which is usually expressed in feet of fluid flowing. Since the units are lb/ft² × 1 ft³/lb = ft, it can also be expressed as ft-lb/lb, or energy per pound of fluid. This means simply that a pound of fluid at any section in a pipe will have the total energy of $p/\gamma + z + v^2/2g$ ft-lb of energy/lb of that fluid, or it may be expressed as a total head in feet of that fluid flowing. Where energy is added by a pump between sections 1 and 2, the modified Bernoulli equation becomes,

$$\frac{p_1}{\gamma} + z_1 + \frac{v_1^2}{2g} + h_a = \frac{p_2}{\gamma} + z_2 + \frac{v_2^2}{2g} + h_f \qquad (4\text{-}3)$$

where h_a represents the energy per pound of fluid added by a pump, h_f represents the energy per pound or head of fluid lost due to friction between sections 1 and 2 in the pipe or conduit.

In Eq. (4-3), v_1 and v_2 represent the average velocities at sections 1 and 2. In order to represent the average kinetic energy per pound of fluid, the average of the velocities squared should be used. For turbulent flow, which is the more usual type of flow encountered in pipe systems, the average of the velocities squared is $1.1\,v^2$, and for laminar flow it is $2\,v^2$, where v is the average velocity at a section. However, since the velocity head, $v^2/2g$, represents such a small proportion of the total head or energy of the flowing fluid, it is customary to use $v^2/2g$ in the Bernoulli equation and neglect the correction factors.

Example 4-4. A 2-ft square tank, 6 ft deep, is full of gasoline ($S_g = 0.65$). With respect to a reference plane at the bottom of the tank, determine the energy contained in 1 lb of gasoline (a) at the surface of the liquid, (b) three feet below the surface, and (c) at the bottom of the tank

Solution: Figure 4-4 is a sketch of the tank. The energy equation for 1 lb of fluid is

$$H = \frac{p}{\gamma} + z + \frac{v^2}{2g}.$$

Therefore, at the surface of the gasoline the energy/lb of gasoline is due only to elevation head, that is,

(a) $H = 0 + 6 + 0 = 6$ ft-lb/lb.

The energy/lb of gasoline at 3 ft below the surface is due to the pressure head and the elevation head, that is

(b) $H = 3 + 3 + 0 = 6$ ft-lb/lb.

The energy/lb of gasoline at the bottom of the tank is due only to pressure head, that is

(c) $H = 6 + 0 + 0 = 6$ ft-lb/lb.

Thus, it appears that the energy per lb of liquid anywhere in the tank is the same, provided the reference plane is not taken above any portion of the liquid.

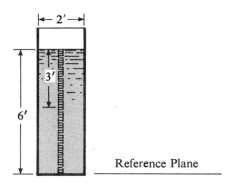

FIGURE 4-4

PROBLEMS

4-21. A 12-in.-diameter pipe contains water at 40 psig. Determine the pressure energy of the water **(a)** per lb of water, and **(b)** per ft of pipe.

4-22. An 8-in.-diameter pipe is carrying water with a velocity of 8 fps. Determine the kinetic energy of the water **(a)** per lb of water, and **(b)** per ft of pipe.

4-23. A tank, 3-ft in diameter and 6 ft deep, is full of gasoline ($\gamma = 42$ pcf). With respect to a reference plane at the bottom of the tank, how much energy is contained in **(a)** one lb of oil at the surface, **(b)** one lb of oil at the bottom of the tank, **(c)** one lb of oil at the center of the tank, and **(d)** the entire tank.

4-24. Water is flowing through a 4-in.-diameter horizontal pipe under a pressure of 8 psig. If the total energy in the water with respect to a reference plane 4 ft below the center of the pipe is 25 ft-lb/lb, determine the discharge.

4-5   HORSEPOWER-HEAD RELATIONSHIP

It is stated in Sec. 4-4 that the head, h_a, added in the Bernoulli equation, can be expressed also as *energy/pound of fluid flowing*, that is, as ft-lb/lb. The total energy added to the flowing stream of fluid in a pipe is obtained by multiplying the energy added per pound by the total pounds of fluid flowing per second past any section of the pipe. Since the discharge per second is expressed by the symbol Q, (cfs), the total weight of fluid passing any section of pipe during any second is expressed by $Q\gamma$, where γ is the weight of the fluid/cubic foot. $Q\gamma$, then, gives the total weight in pounds per second delivered by a pump. Therefore, the total energy delivered to the fluid by a pump can be expressed as $Q\gamma h_a$, that is,

$$\text{total input energy} = Q\gamma h_a.$$

In the Bernoulli equation, the head added, h_a, appears on the left side of the equality sign as indicated in Eq. (4-3). Since one horsepower is 550 ft-lb/sec of energy, the horsepower input into a stream of liquid by a pump is

$$\text{hp} = \frac{Q\gamma h_a}{550}.$$

Example 4-5.   An open, semicircular flume, having a radius of 5 ft, is flowing full and has an average velocity of 6 ft/second. Determine the total horsepower available in the water with respect to a reference plane 10 ft below the bottom of the flume.

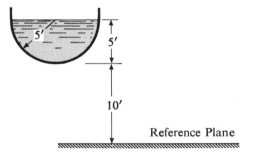

FIGURE 4-5

Solution: Example 4-4 shows that the energy per lb of liquid is the same anywhere in a tank with respect to a reference plane that is below any portion of the liquid. Therefore, the energy per lb of water in Fig. 4-5 can be taken at the surface of the flume and expressed as

$$H = 0 + 15 + \frac{6^2}{64.4} = 15.56 \text{ ft-lb/lb}$$

and, since the total energy in the flowing flume is $Q\gamma H$,

$$H_t = \frac{25\pi}{2} 6(62.4)15.56 = 228{,}700 \text{ ft-lb/second.}$$

Therefore,

$$\text{hp(available)} = \frac{H_t}{550} = \frac{228,700}{550} = 416.$$

Example 4-6. A 30-hp pump is placed in a 6-in.-diameter line that is discharging 2.51 cfs of gasoline ($S_g = 0.68$). The pipe line has a submerged discharge in a closed tank. The oil level in the tank is 20 ft above the suction side of the pump where a vacuum gage indicates 9 in. of mercury vacuum. If the head loss from the suction side of the pump to the tank is 12 ft of oil, determine the pressure on the surface of the oil in the closed tank.

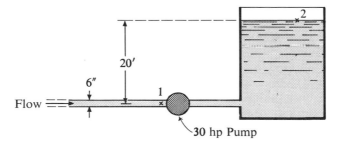

FIGURE 4-6

Solution: Figure 4-6 indicates a possible arrangement for the pump and tank. The velocity of the gasoline in the pipe is

$$v = \frac{Q}{a} = 2.51 \frac{16}{\pi} = 12.8 \text{ fps.}$$

A vacuum of 9 in. of mercury in terms of feet of gasoline is

$$\frac{p_1}{\gamma} = \frac{-9}{12} \frac{13.6(0.433)}{0.68(0.433)} = -15.00 \text{ ft of gasoline.}$$

The head added by the pump, assuming no loss, can be determined from the equation, hp $= Q\gamma h_a/550$. Thus,

$$h_a = \frac{550(\text{hp})}{Q\gamma} = \frac{550(30)}{2.51(62.4)0.68} = 155.$$

Now, substituting all known values into the Bernoulli equation gives,

$$-15.00 + 0 + \frac{12.8^2}{64.4} + 155 = \frac{p_2}{0.68(0.433)} + 20 + 0 + 12$$

and

$$\frac{p_2}{0.294} = -15.00 + 2.56 + 155 - 32 = 110.56.$$

Therefore,

$$p_2 = 0.294(110.56) = 32.5 \text{ psig.}$$

PROBLEMS

4-25. Oil ($S_g = 0.80$) flows through a horizontal 3-in.-diameter pipe under a pressure of 21 psig at the rate of 0.63 cfs. Determine **(a)** the total energy available per lb of oil with respect to a reference plane at the center of the pipe, and **(b)** the horsepower available with respect to the same reference plane.

4-26. The discharge through a turbine below a dam is 6000 cfs. Determine the available horsepower if the head is 120 ft.

4-27. A 40-hp pump delivers water from a reservoir into an elevated tank, as shown in Fig. P 4-27. If the head loss between the reservoir and the tank is 16 ft of water, determine the discharge when the surface of the water in the tank is 90 ft above the surface of the water in the reservoir.

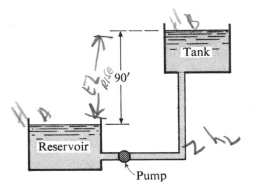

FIGURE P 4-27

4-28. A 25-hp pump delivers 2.38 cfs of oil ($\gamma = 50$ pcf) through a 4-in.-diameter line into the bottom of a closed tank, as shown in Fig. P 4-28. The oil level in the tank is 12 ft above the pump suction line and the head loss in the line from the suction side of the pump to the tank is

10 ft of oil. The vacuum gage on the suction pipe at the pump registers 6 in. of mercury vacuum. Determine the pressure on the surface of the oil in the closed tank.

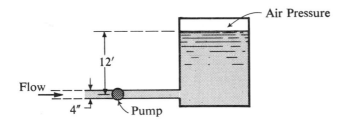

FIGURE P 4-28

4-29. A pump draws oil ($S_g = 0.90$) through a 10-in. suction line and discharges it through a 6-in. line into the bottom of a large storage tank at the rate of 1.57 cfs, as shown in Fig. P 4-29. The base of the tank is 10 ft above the pump. A gage in the discharge line at the pump indicates a pressure of 14.0 psig. The head loss in the pipe from the pump to the tank is 20 ft of oil. Determine the approximate depth of the oil in the tank.

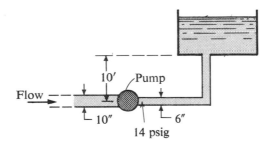

FIGURE P 4-29

4-30. Water from a reservoir flows through a pipe line. The flow terminates at a nozzle that discharges a 2-in.-diameter jet at a point 150 ft below the water level in the reservoir, as shown in Fig. P 4-30. The jet supplies a turbine that has an overall efficiency of 83 percent. (The power developed by the turbine is 0.83 of the power delivered by the jet.) Assume a friction loss of 30 ft of water in the pipe line and nozzle. Determine the power developed by the turbine.

4-31. A pump delivers oil ($S_g = 0.93$) at the rate of 6.28 cfs. The horizontal suction and discharge pipes leading to the pump have the same diameter.

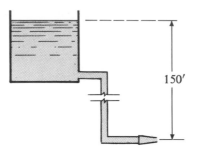

FIGURE P 4-30

A vacuum gage on the suction side of the pump indicates 12 in. of mercury vacuum, while the pressure gage on the discharge side of the pump reads 24 psig. Determine the horsepower delivered by the pump.

4-32. The suction pipe to a pump is 8 in. in diameter and the discharge pipe is 6 in. in diameter. A gage on the suction line, located 4 ft below the pump, indicates a vacuum of 8 in. of mercury and the pressure gage on the discharge line, 8 ft below the pump, indicates a pressure of 26 psi, as shown in Fig. P 4-32. The power input to the pump is 30 hp, and the head loss in the pipe between gages is 12 ft of water when the discharge is 2.35 cfs of water. Determine the efficiency of the pump.

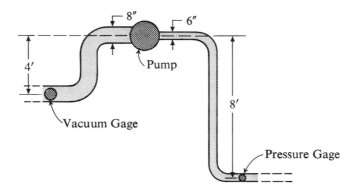

FIGURE P 4-32

4-33. A pump takes water through an 8-in. suction pipe and delivers it into a reservoir at the rate of 1.57 cfs through a 6-in. pipe, as shown in Fig. P 4-33. At the suction side of the pump a vacuum gage registers 9 in. of mercury. What horsepower must be delivered by the pump if the friction loss from the suction side of the pump to the reservoir is 10 psig?

4-34. Water is pumped from a settling basin into an upper reservoir through 1200 ft of 8-in.-diameter cast iron pipe. The pump delivers 35 hp. See Fig. P 4-34. The head loss in the pipe is 12 ft of water. Determine the approximate vertical distance between the surfaces of the basin and reservoir if the discharge is 1.57 cfs.

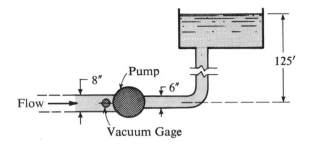

FIGURE P 4-33

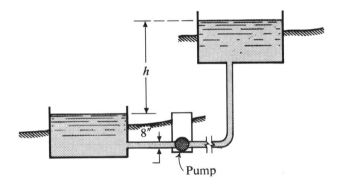

FIGURE P 4-34

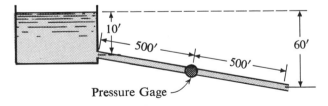

FIGURE P 4-35

4-35. Water flows from a large tank through 1000 ft of 6-in. pipe and develops a head loss of 0.03 ft/ft of pipe length, as shown in Fig. P 4-35. Determine **(a)** the discharge, and **(b)** the reading on the pressure gage.

4-36. Water is pumped from a lower reservoir into the bottom of an upper reservoir through 1000 ft of 6-in. pipe at the rate of 2.0 cfs, as shown in Fig. P 4-36. The difference in water levels between the two reservoirs is 235 ft and the head loss in the pipe line is 40 ft of water. Determine the required horsepower.

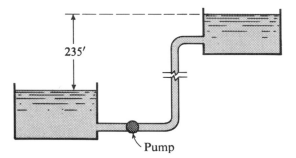

FIGURE P 4-36

4-37. A pump draws water through an 8-in. suction line, and discharges it through a 6-in. line at a velocity of 8 fps, as shown in Fig. P 4-37. At point A in the suction line, the pressure is -7 psig. At point B in the discharge line, 10 ft above point A, the pressure is 45 psi. What horsepower is delivered by the pump? Neglect friction losses.

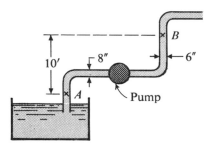

FIGURE P 4-37

Chapter 5

Major and Minor Losses in Pipe Flow

5-1 MAJOR HEAD LOSS—LAMINAR FLOW

As stated earlier in this text, particles of fluid flowing in a closed conduit have different velocities, In turbulent flow the particles move in various, unpredictable directions. Under laminar flow the particles move in paths parallel to the direction of flow and the velocity of the particles will vary

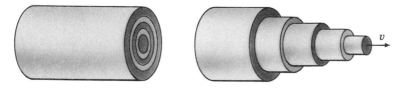

FIGURE 5-1

from zero at the sides of the pipe to a maximum velocity at the center. If a group of streamlines are taken symmetrically with respect to the center of the pipe, they form a stream tube, as shown in Fig. 5-1. Since each stream tube moves at a different velocity, frictional resistance to the relative motion of the stream tubes is developed due to the viscosity of the fluid and also due to the surface tension at the boundary of the fluid.

Note: The following discussion involves calculus.

In order to rationally evaluate this resistance, or frictional force, a horizontal differential length of the fluid, symmetrical with respect to the center of the pipe, is removed from the pipe, as shown in Fig. 5-2(a), to form the free-body diagram shown in Fig. 5-2(b). The diameter of the pipe and the diameter of the differential element are assumed to be constant.

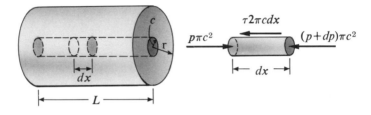

FIGURE 5-2

The pressure is assumed to increase to the right in the direction of flow by the increment of pressure dp in the distance dx. The frictional resistance on the surface of the element is $\tau 2\pi c \, dx$. Since the diameter of the pipe is constant, the velocity at each end of the element is the same. Therefore, a static condition prevails and the fluid is in equilibrium. Thus, by $\sum \mathbf{F}_x = 0$,

$$p\pi c^2 - (p + dp)\pi c^2 - \tau 2\pi c \, dx = 0.$$

By cancellation,

$$-dp\pi c^2 = \tau 2\pi c \, dx$$

or

$$-c \, dp = 2\tau \, dx.$$

However, from Eq. (1-1),

$$\tau = -\mu \frac{\Delta v}{\Delta c}$$

and, as Δc approaches zero,

$$\tau = -\mu \frac{dv}{dc}$$

so

$$c \, dp = 2\mu \frac{dv}{dc} dx$$

or

$$\int_0^r c \, dc \int_{p_1}^{p_2} dp = 2\mu \int_{v_0}^{v_c} dv \int_0^L dx.$$

Integrating this equation gives

$$\frac{r^2}{2} (p_2 - p_1) = -2\mu L(v_0 - v_c).$$

Since $v_c = 0$ at the inside wall of the pipe,

$$(p_1 - p_2) \frac{r^2}{2} = 2\mu L v_0,$$

where v_0 is the velocity at the center of the pipe and, also, the maximum velocity. For laminar flow the distribution of velocity across a section of flowing fluid in a circular pipe is parabolic. Thus the average velocity for the entire cross section is one-half the maximum velocity, v_0. Thus

$$v_0 = 2v,$$

where v is the average velocity in the cross section of the flowing fluid. Therefore,

$$p_1 - p_2 = 8\mu L \frac{v}{r^2}. \tag{5-1}$$

The Bernoulli equation for the length of pipe from which this element was taken is

$$\frac{p_1}{w} + z_1 + \frac{v_1^2}{2g} = \frac{p_2}{w} + z_2 + \frac{v_2^2}{2g} + h_f.$$

However, since the diameters of the pipe at points 1 and 2 are the same, the velocities at these points are the same and may be cancelled out of the equation. Also, taking the reference plane through the center of the pipe reduces z_1 and z_2 to zero. With these cancellations, the Bernoulli equation becomes

$$\frac{p_1}{\gamma} - \frac{p_2}{\gamma} = h_f.$$

Substituting Eq. (5-1) into this equation gives

$$h_f = \frac{8\mu L v}{\gamma r^2}.$$

But $\gamma = \rho g$, and $r = d/2$, where d is the diameter of the pipe.

This frictional resistance, h_f, becomes,

$$h_f = \frac{32\mu L v}{\rho g d^2} = \frac{64\mu L v^2}{\rho v d^2 2g}. \tag{5-2}$$

Equation (5-2) is known as the Poiseuille equation, and may be written,

$$h_f = \frac{64}{\rho v d/u} \frac{L}{d} \frac{v^2}{2g} \tag{5-3}$$

in which the term $\rho v d/u$, a dimensionless factor, is called the Reynolds number, N_r.

Equation (5-3) indicates that the head loss in a pipe flowing with laminar flow is proportional to the pipe length and the velocity head, and is inversely proportional to the diameter of the pipe and to the Reynolds number, N_r.

5-2 MAJOR HEAD LOSS—TURBULENT FLOW

In addition to the resistance between particles in the direction of flow, turbulent flow produces a considerable amount of resistance due to particles of fluid moving or having components of velocity in the transverse direction of flow. Since it is impossible, rationally, to evaluate this additional energy loss, a factor, f, based on experimentally determined results, is introduced into the head loss equation to replace the $64/N_r$ factor. The term, f, is a coefficient of friction and its value is determined by the roughness of the pipe and the Reynolds number. Thus, the head loss for turbulent flow becomes,

$$h_f = f \frac{L}{d} \frac{v^2}{2g}.$$

The Moody diagram, Fig. 5-3, developed from experimentally determined values, shows the values of f for smooth pipe and for various degrees of relative roughness, K/d, of various kinds of pipe.

The value of $f = 64/N_r$ for laminar flow, plotted as a straight line on the logarithmic paper of Fig. 5-3, is shown on the left side of the Moody diagram. In the transition region, where the Reynolds number varies from 2100 to 3000, the flow can be either laminar or turbulent. To be on the safe side, the Reynolds number of 2100 is used in the following problems to separate laminar and turbulent flow since values of Reynolds number below 2100 are always laminar.

Values of the roughness coefficient K for the determination of K/d are given in Table 4. Both K and d on the Moody diagram are in inches.

TABLE 4

Type of Pipe	K
Asphalted Cast Iron	0.005
Cast Iron	0.010
Concrete	0.012–0.120
Drawn Tubing	0.00006
Galvanized Iron	0.006
Riveted Steel	0.036–0.36
Steel or Wrought Iron	0.0017
Wood Stave	0.007–0.036

5-3 PROCEDURE WITH THE REYNOLDS NUMBER KNOWN

When sufficient data is given to allow for the initial evaluation of the Reynolds number, the major head loss, h_f, readily can be determined and used in the Bernoulli equation. The following examples illustrate this procedure.

Example 5-1.   Water, having a density of 1.934 slugs/cu ft and a viscosity of 20.98(10^{-6}) slugs/ft-sec, flows through a 4-in.-diameter pipe at the rate of 2.4 cfs. Determine the Reynolds number.

Solution: Determine the velocity as

$$v = \frac{Q}{a} = 2.4 \frac{36}{\pi} = 27.5 \text{ fps.}$$

Therefore, the Reynolds number, $\rho v d/\mu$, is

$$N_r = 1.934(27.5) \frac{10^6}{20.98} \frac{1}{3} = 845{,}000.$$

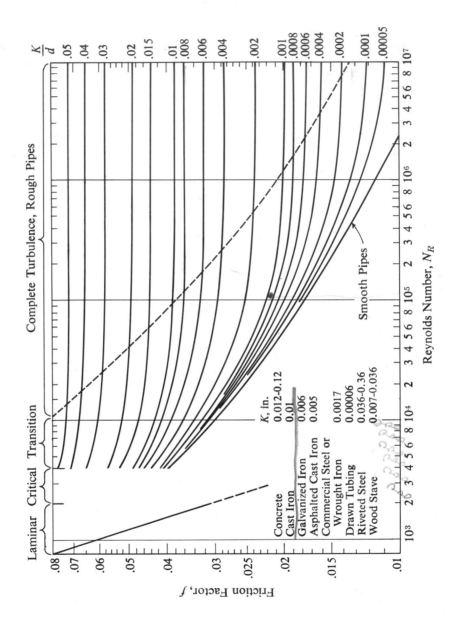

MOODY DIAGRAM

FIGURE 5-3

Example 5-2. Gasoline [$\rho = 1.32$ slugs/cu ft; $\mu = 6.5(10^{-6})$ slugs/ft-sec] flows through a 6-in.-diameter commercial steel pipe at the rate of 3.14 cfs. Determine the head loss in 200 ft of pipe.

Solution: The coefficient of roughness, K, for commercial steel pipe is 0.0017. Therefore,

$$\frac{K}{d} = \frac{0.0017}{6} = 0.00028.$$

The velocity is

$$v = \frac{Q}{a} = 3.14\frac{16}{\pi} = 16 \text{ fps.}$$

The Reynolds number is

$$N_r = \frac{\rho v d}{\mu} = 1.32(16)\tfrac{1}{2}\frac{10^6}{6.5} = 1.625(10^6).$$

From the Moody diagram, $f = 0.015$. Therefore, the head loss is

$$h_f = f\frac{L}{d}\frac{v^2}{2g} = \frac{0.015(200)16^2}{\tfrac{1}{2}(64.4)} = 23.9 \text{ ft of gasoline}$$

Example 5-3. Kerosene [$\rho = 1.57$ slugs/cu ft; $\mu = 40(10^{-6})$ slugs/ft-sec] is pumped from a large open reservoir through 600 ft of 3-in.-diameter cast iron pipe and discharges into the air above a tank at the rate of 0.785 cfs. If the discharge end of the pipe is 40 ft above the surface of the reservoir, what horsepower input into the flowing gasoline is required?

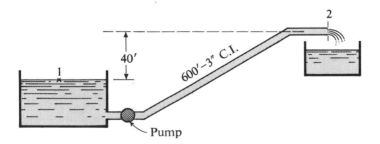

FIGURE 5-4

Solution: Figure 5-4 shows a possible arrangement of the pump and tanks. The velocity is

$$v = \frac{Q}{a} = 0.785\frac{64}{\pi} = 16 \text{ fps.}$$

The Reynolds number is

$$N_r = \frac{\rho v d}{\mu} = 1.57(16)\frac{1}{4}\frac{10^6}{40} = 157,000.$$

The coefficient of roughness, K, equals 0.010, and

$$\frac{K}{d} = \frac{0.010}{3} = 0.0033.$$

From the Moody diagram, $f = 0.0276$. Therefore, the head loss is

$$h_f \frac{0.0276(600)}{\frac{1}{4}}\frac{16^2}{64.4} = 263 \text{ ft of kerosene.}$$

Substituting these other known values into the Bernoulli equation, written from points 1 to 2, gives,

$$0 + 0 + 0 + h_a = 0 + 40 + \frac{16^2}{64.4} + 263.$$

Therefore,
$$h_a = 307 \text{ ft of kerosene.}$$

Since,

$$\text{hp} = \frac{Q\gamma h_a}{550},$$

$$\text{hp} = \frac{0.785(1.57)32.2(307)}{550} = 22.2.$$

PROBLEMS

5-1. Water at 59°F flows through a 3-in.-diameter pipe at the rate of 1.25 cfs. Determine the Reynolds number.

5-2. Fuel oil (cracked) at 70°F flows through a 2-in.-diameter pipe at the rate of 0.50 cfs. Determine the Reynolds number.

5-3. If the Reynolds number for glycerine, flowing through a 1-in.-diameter pipe at 100°F, is 250, determine the velocity.

5-4. If the Reynolds number for brine at 60°F, flowing through a 4-in.-diameter pipe, is 250,000, determine the velocity.

5-5. At what least velocity should the flow of water at 68°F in a 3-in.-diameter pipe become turbulent?

5-6. What is the critical velocity for castor oil at 59°F in a 6-in.-diameter pipe?

5-7. Determine the largest diameter pipe in which the flow of Mobil oil "A" at 100°F will be laminar at a velocity of 3 fps.

5-8. Determine the critical velocity of nitrogen at 32°F in a 2-in.-diameter tube.

5-9. Determine the head loss in 500 ft of 12-in.-diameter cast iron pipe carrying 9 cfs of water at 68°F.

5-10. Determine the head loss in 200 ft of 4-in.-diameter commercial steel pipe carrying 1.0 cfs of kerosene at 60°F.

5-11. Determine the slope at which a 3-in.-diameter wrought iron pipe carrying 0.785 cfs of water at 68°F must be laid if the pressure is to remain constant throughout the length of the pipe.

5-12. Crude oil "B" at 60°F flows through a horizontal 8-in.-diameter galvanized iron pipe at the rate of 6 cfs. Determine the head loss per foot of pipe.

5-13. Two reservoirs are connected by 2000 ft of 12-in. smooth concrete pipe, as shown in Fig. P 5-13. If water at 32°F flows from one reservoir to the other at the rate of 16 cfs, determine the probable difference in elevation between the water surfaces in the two reservoirs.

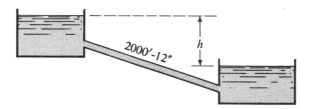

FIGURE P 5-13

5-14. Water at 32°F is to be pumped through 400 ft of 2-in.-diameter wrought iron pipe from a well that is 250 ft deep into a standpipe at the rate of 180 gpm. The pipe discharges into the air at a point 125 ft above the ground. Determine the horsepower required.

5-15. A cylindrical standpipe, 16 ft in diameter and 24 ft high, is filled by pumping water, at 32°F, at the rate of 3.14 cfs from a well through 5000 ft of 6-in.-diameter commercial steel pipe and discharges into the air at the top of the standpipe, 200 ft above the bottom of the well. If power is supplied to a pumping unit with an efficiency of 75 percent, determine the cost to fill the standpipe at a power charge of 1.25 cents/kwhr.

5-16. Furnace oil at 60°F is pumped from a large supply tank through 300 ft of 3-in.-diameter wrought iron pipe and discharges into the air above another tank. The pump is located just outside the first tank and 30 ft below the discharge end of the pipe, as shown in Fig. P 5-16. Determine the pressure that is required on the discharge side of the pump to maintain a discharge of 0.63 cfs.

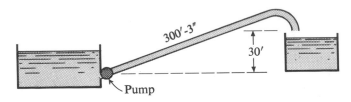

FIGURE P 5-16

5-17. If the pump in Prob. 5-16 is 8 ft below the surface of the oil in the supply tank, what horsepower must it develop?

5-18. Water is pumped through 10 miles of 12-in.-diameter commercial steel pipe at the rate of 12.57 cfs. The water is pumped up a grade of 10 ft/mile. Determine the power required when the temperature of the water is (a) 59°F, and (b) 32°F.

5-19. A horizontal 6-in.-diameter cast iron pipe, 1600 ft long, carries 1.57 cfs of water at 68°F. Determine the frictional head loss.

5-20 A horizontal 24-in.-diameter cast iron pipe discharges water at 32°F at the rate of 8 mgd. Determine the frictional head loss per 1000 ft. of pipe.

5-4 PROCEDURE WITH THE REYNOLDS NUMBER UNKNOWN

When insufficient data is given to allow for the initial evaluation of the Reynolds number (generally when the velocity or diameter of the pipe is unknown), the value of f cannot readily be determined. In this case the value of f is assumed, usually at 0.020, and later checked, using a trial-and-error method. When the computed value of f is within 10 percent of the last assumed value, no further computations are necessary. The procedure for solving problems when the Reynolds number is unknown is illustrated in the following examples.

Example 5-4. Water at 32°F ($\rho/\mu = 51,700$) is to be pumped through a new galvanized iron pipe, 800 ft long, at the rate of 3 cfs. What diameter of pipe is required if the friction loss is not to exceed 16 ft of water?

Solution: Assume $f = 0.020$. Then, since

$$h_f = f\frac{L}{d}\frac{v^2}{2g},$$

$$16 = 0.020\frac{(800)}{d}\frac{v^2}{2g}.$$

However,

$$v = \frac{Q}{a} = \frac{3(4)}{\pi d^2} = \frac{12}{\pi d^2}.$$

Substituting in the friction equation, gives

$$16 = 0.020 \frac{(800)}{d} \frac{144}{\pi^2 d^4 64.4}.$$

and

$$d^5 = \frac{16(144)}{9.87(16)64.4} = 0.227.$$

Therefore.

$$d = 0.742 \text{ ft.}$$

Since f was assumed, it must now be checked. An error of 10 percent is allowed. Using the diameter computed above,

$$v = \frac{12}{\pi d^2} = \frac{12}{\pi 0.742^2} = 6.93 \text{ fps.}$$

Therefore,

$$N_r = 51,700(6.93)0.742 = 266,000$$

$$\frac{K}{d} = \frac{0.006}{0.742(12)} = 0.000673.$$

From the Moody diagram, $f = 0.0193$. Since this is within the 10 percent of the assumed value of 0.20, the minimum diameter of 0.742 ft or 8.9 in. is satisfactory. In this case a nominal 10-in.-diameter pipe would be used since the next lower size is 8 in.

Example 5-5.   A 40-hp pump, with an efficiency of 80 percent, pumps water [$\rho = 1.937$ slugs/cu ft; $\mu = 23.83(10^{-6})$ slugs/ft-sec] from one reservoir into another through 600 ft of 6-in.-diameter smooth concrete pipe, as shown in Fig. 5-5. Determine the discharge in cfs.

Solution: After selecting points 1 and 2, as shown in Fig. 5-5, write the Bernoulli equation between these points and substitute all known values. Thus,

$$0 + 0 + 0 + h_a = 0 + 0 + 0 + h_f.$$

Therefore,

$$h_a = h_f.$$

The term h_a can be expressed in the power equation in terms of the unknown velocity. Thus,

$$\text{hp} = \frac{Q\gamma h_a}{550} \quad \text{and} \quad h_a = \frac{550(40)0.80(16)}{1.937(32.2)\pi v} = \frac{1437}{v}.$$

The Reynolds number, N_r, also may be expressed in terms of the velocity. Thus,

$$N_r = 1.937v \frac{\frac{1}{2}10^6}{23.83} = 40{,}700v.$$

Since N_r is unknown, assume $f = 0.020$. Thus,

$$h_f = 0.020 \frac{(600)v^2}{\frac{1}{2}2g} = 0.020(18.63)v^2 = 0.373v^2.$$

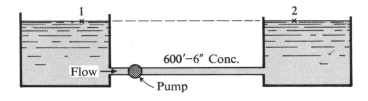

FIGURE 5-5

Substituting back into the Bernoulli equation,

$$0.373v^2 = \frac{1437}{v}$$

$$v^3 = 3852.5$$

and

$$v = 15.7 \text{ fps.}$$

$$N_r = \frac{1.937(10^6)15.7}{2(23.83)}$$

Check:

$$N_r = 40{,}700(15.7) = 638{,}000$$

$$\frac{K}{d} = \frac{0.012}{6} = 0.002.$$

Therefore, from the Moody diagram, $f = 0.024$. Since this f is more than 10 percent greater than the assumed f of 0.020, a new value of velocity will be necessary.

Assume $f = 0.024$. Then,

$$h_f = 0.024(18.63)v^2 = 0.447v^2.$$

Again, substitute back into the Bernoulli equation.

$$0.447v^2 = \frac{1437}{v}$$

and

$$v = 14.3 \text{ fps.}$$

Again, check the Reynolds number.

$$N_r = 40,700(14.8) = 581,000$$

and $f = 0.024$, which checks with the assumed value. Therefore, the velocity is correct and

$$Q = av = \frac{\pi}{16}(14.3) = 2.80 \text{ cfs.}$$

PROBLEMS

5-21. Determine the probable discharge of water at 32°F through a 12-in.-diameter horizontal concrete pipe in good condition. The loss of head in a 2000-ft length is 20 ft.

5-22. What diameter of new horizontal wood-stave pipe should be installed to carry 25 cfs of water at 59°F a distance of 2 miles with a loss of head of 15 ft?

5-23. Two pressure gages 1000 ft apart in a horizontal 4-in.-diameter cast iron pipe, which carries medium lubricating oil at 70°F, indicate a difference of pressure of 25 psi. Determine the discharge.

5-24. A new 6-in.-galvanized iron pipe, carrying water at 32°F, is laid on an upgrade of 1.6 ft in 1000 ft and discharges into the air. If the gage pressure 1000 ft from the discharge end of the pipe is 20 psi, determine the probable discharge.

5-25. A 35-hp pump, having an efficiency of 83 percent, pumps water at 68°F from a lake through 500 ft of 8-in. wrought iron pipe and discharges into the air over a reservoir 200 ft above the surface of the lake, as shown in Fig. P 5-25. Determine the discharge.

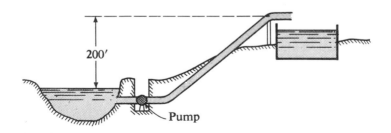

200'

Pump

FIGURE P 5-25

5-26. A pump, installed in a 6-in.-diameter cast iron pipe, discharges 4.0 cfs of water at 100°F. If the 6-in. line is to be used for cracked fuel oil at 100°F and the efficiency of the pump does not change, determine the discharge of fuel oil that may be expected.

5-27. A pipe line, 25,000 ft long, is to deliver 24 cfs of water at 32°F. The surface of the receiving tank is 60 ft below the level of the reservoir, as shown in Fig. P 5-27, and a total of 2000 hp is available. What size of new wrought iron pipe should be used?

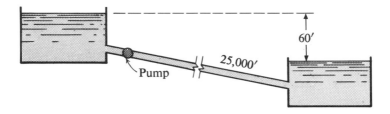

FIGURE P 5-27

5-28. Fuel oil [$S_g = 0.854$; kinematic viscosity, $\nu = 412(10^{-7})$ sq ft/sec] flows through 2000 ft of 6-in. commercial steel pipe from an open tank to the bottom of an open reservoir. The difference in the elevation of the oil surfaces is 160 ft. Determine the discharge.

5-29. Water [$\nu = 0.0000123$ sq ft/sec; $\gamma = 62.37$ pcf] is pumped through 1000 ft of 6-in.-diameter cast iron pipe from one reservoir into another, as shown in Fig. P 5-29. If the pump delivers 15 hp, determine the probable discharge in cfs.

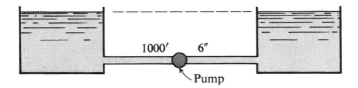

FIGURE P 5-29

5-30. Lubricating oil [$\nu = 85.6(10^{-6})$ sq ft/sec; $\gamma = 57$ pcf] is pumped through 2000 ft of 4-in.-diameter commercial steel pipe from one reservoir into another, as shown in Fig. P 5-30. If the pump adds 50 hp to the fluid, determine the probable discharge in cfs.

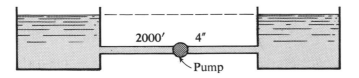

FIGURE P 5-30

5-31. A 40-hp pump draws water [$\nu = 1.25(10^{-5})$ sq ft/sec; $\gamma = 62.37$ pcf] through 1200 ft of 8-in.-diameter commercial steel pipe from a reservior and discharges it into a tank, as shown in Fig. P 5-31. Determine the discharge in cfs.

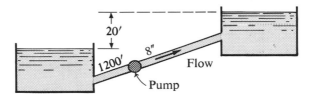

FIGURE P 5-31

5-32. A 50-hp pump draws water [$\nu = 2.0(10^{-5})$ sq ft/sec] through 600 ft of 4-in.-diameter commercial steel pipe from a reservoir and discharges into the bottom of a tank. The water level in the reservoir and the tank are at the same elevation, as shown in Fig. P 5-32. Determine the discharge.

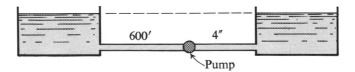

FIGURE P 5-32

5-33. Water at 32°F is pumped at the rate of 1.57 cfs from one large open tank into another through a 6-in.-diameter cast iron pipe 400 ft long. The water level in the second tank is 160 ft above the level in the first tank and the discharge end of the pipe is submerged. If 40 hp is delivered to the pump unit, determine the efficiency of the pump.

5-34. Water at 32°F flows by gravity from one reservoir into another through 2000 ft of 12-in.-diameter clean cast iron pipe. The difference in elevation of the water surfaces in the two reservoirs is 100 ft and the discharge end of the pipe is submerged. Determine the discharge in cfs.

5-35. Gasoline [$\rho = 1.32$ slugs/cu ft; $\mu = 6.5(10^{-6})$ slugs/ft-sec] flows by gravity from a large open reservoir through 1000 ft of clean copper tubing into the bottom of a large supply tank at the rate of 1.57 cfs. The fluid level in the supply tank is 100 ft below the fluid level in the reservoir. Determine the required diameter for the copper tubing.

5-36. Water flows through 2000 ft of new 2-in.-diameter steel pipe from a large open reservoir into a large closed tank in which the pressure above the water surface is 4 in. of mercury vacuum, as shown in Fig. P 5-36. The water level in the reservoir is 25 ft above the water level in the tank. Determine the discharge when both ends of the pipe are submerged. The ratio of the density to viscosity of the water is 51,700 sec/ft^2.

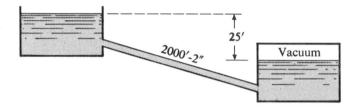

25′

2000′-2″

Vacuum

FIGURE P 5-36

5-37. Water is to be pumped through a new asphalted horizontal cast iron pipe 6000 ft long at the rate of 4.51 cfs. Determine the diameter of the required pipe if the friction loss is not to exceed 75 ft of water.

5-38. Two reservoirs are connected by 1500 ft of old 6-in.-diameter riveted steel pipe ($K = 0.24$) which discharges 2.0 cfs of water. It is necessary to double the discharge by replacing the old pipe with new riveted steel pipe. What diameter of pipe will be required?

5-39. Three parallel 4-in.-diameter wrought iron pipes connect two reservoirs 5000 ft apart with a difference in surface elevation of 40 ft, as shown in Fig. P 5-39. Determine the size of one wrought iron pipe that will give the same discharge of water as the three pipes.

5-40. An 80-hp pump is to be used to pump kerosene at 60°F through 2000 ft of horizontal cast iron pipe. Determine the diameter of the required pipe if the discharge is to be 3.0 cfs.

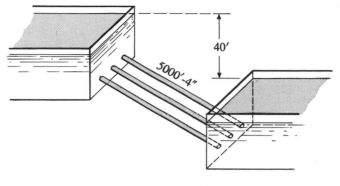

FIGURE P 5-39

5-41. Water flows from a reservoir through 1500 ft of new 24-in.-diameter concrete pipe to discharge into the air at a point 30 ft below the water surface in the reservoir. Determine the discharge in cfs.

5-42. Determine the horsepower required to pump 20 cfs of water at 32°F from one tank into another tank that is 300 ft higher. The water will flow through 2400 ft of old 18-in.-diameter concrete pipe ($K = 0.12$) as shown in Fig. P 5-42.

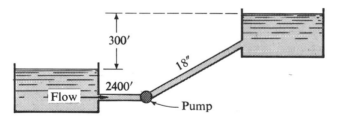

FIGURE P 5-42

5-5 MINOR LOSSES

Loss of head occurs in a pipe line whenever a change in velocity, either in magnitude or direction, occurs. Such losses occur in valves, tees, ells, crosses, nozzles, orifices, short tubes, or at the intersection of pipes of different sizes. Generally, the loss is expressed as a coefficient multiplied by the velocity head, as $Kv^2/2g$, or it can be expressed in terms of an equivalent length of pipe. Fig. 5-6 gives the coefficients of the velocity head, K, based on the velocity in the smaller pipe where a sudden enlargement or sudden

TABLE 5
REPRESENTATIVE EQUIVALENT LENGTH IN PIPE DIAMETERS (L/d) OF VARIOUS VALVES AND FITTINGS*

		Description of Product		Equivalent Length in Pipe Diameters (L/d)
Globe Valves	Stem Perpendicular to Run	With no obstruction in flat, bevel, or plug type seat	Fully open	340
		With wing or pin guided disc	Fully open	450
	Y-Pattern	(No obstruction in flat, bevel, or plug type seat)		
		— With stem 60° from run of pipe line	Fully open	175
		— With stem 45° from run of pipe line	Fully open	145
	Angle Valves	With no obstruction in flat, bevel, or plug type seat	Fully open	145
		With wing or pin guided disc	Fully open	200
Gate Valves	Wedge, Disc, Double Disc, or Plug Disc		Fully open	13
			Three-quarters open	35
			One-half open	160
			One-quarter open	900
	Pulp Stock		Fully open	17
			Three-quarters open	50
			One-half open	260
			One-quarter open	1200
	Conduit Pipe Line Gate, Ball, and Plug Valves		Fully open	3†
Check Valves	Conventional Swing		0.5‡ ... Fully open	135
	Clearway Swing		0.5‡ ... Fully open	50
	Globe Lift or Stop; Stem Perpendicular to Run or Y-Pattern		2.0‡ ... Fully open	Same as Globe
	Angle Lift or Stop		2.0‡ ... Fully open	Same as Angle
	In-Line Ball		2.5 vertical and 0.25 horizontal‡ ... Fully open	150

	Description of Product		Equivalent Length in Pipe Diameters (L/d)
Foot Valves with Strainer	With poppet lift-type disc	0.3‡...Fully open	420
	With leather-hinged disc	0.4‡...Fully open	75
Butterfly Valves (8-inch and larger)		Fully open	40
Cocks	Straight-Through	Rectangular plug port area equal to 100% of pipe area Fully open	18
	Three-Way	Rectangular plug port area equal to 80% of pipe area (fully open) Flow straight through	44
		Flow through branch	140
Fittings	90° Standard Elbow		30
	45° Standard Elbow		16
	90° Long Radius Elbow		20
	90° Street Elbow		50
	45° Street Elbow		26
	Square Corner Elbow		57
	Standard Tee	With flow through run	20
		With flow through branch	60
	Close Pattern Return Bend		50
Pipe	Sudden Enlargements and Contractions		See page 110
	90° Pipe Bends		See page 111
	Miter Bends		See page 112
	Entrance and Exit Losses		See page 113

* Reproduced from Technical Paper #410, *Flow of Fluids*, Courtesy of Crane Co.

† Exact equivalent length is equal to the length between flange faces or welding ends.

‡ Minimum calculated pressure drop (psi) across valve to provide sufficient flow to lift disc fully.

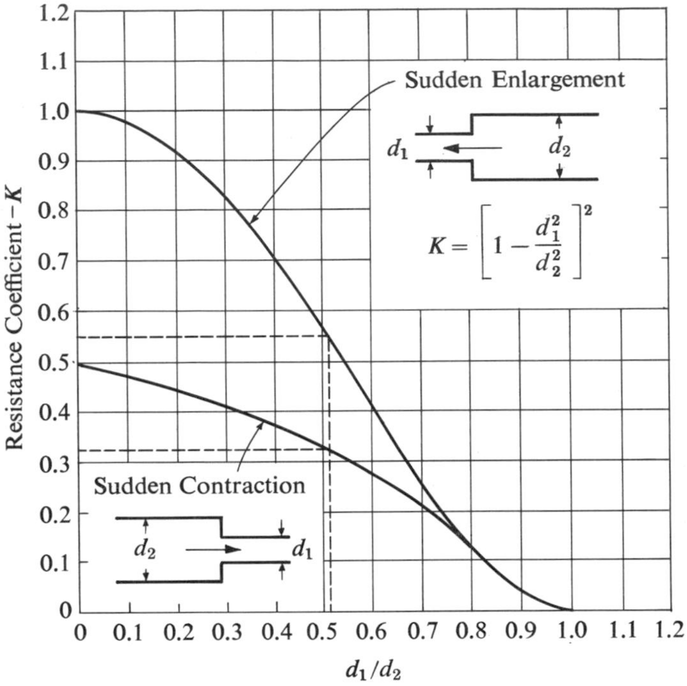

FIGURE 5-6

Sudden Enlargement: The resistance coefficient, K, for a sudden enlargement from 6-in. Schedule 40 pipe to 12-in. Schedule 40 pipe is 0.55, based on the 6-in. pipe size.

$$\frac{d_1}{d_2} = \frac{6.065}{11.938} = 0.51.$$

Sudden Contraction: The resistance coefficient, K, for a sudden contraction from 12-in. Schedule 40 pipe to 6-in. Schedule 40 pipe is 0.33, based on the 6-in. pipe size.

$$\frac{d_1}{d_2} = \frac{6.065}{11.938} = 0.51.$$

NOTE: The values for the resistance coefficient, K, are based on velocity in the small pipe. To determine K values in terms of the greater diameter, multiply the chart values by (d_2/d_1).

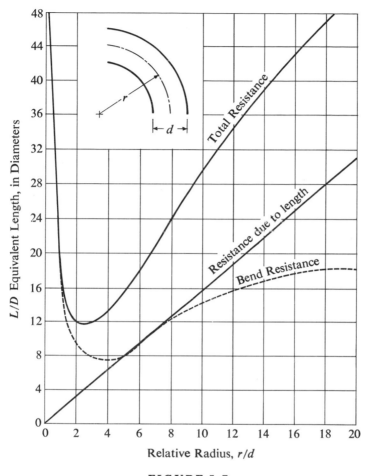

FIGURE 5-7

The chart above shows the resistance of 90° bends to the flow of fluids in terms of equivalent lengths of straight pipe. Resistance of bends greater than 90° is found using the formula:

$$\frac{L}{d} = R_t + (n - 1)\left(R_l + \frac{R_b}{2}\right),$$

where n = total number of 90° bends in coil
R_t = total resistance due to one 90° bend, in L/d
R_l = resistance due to length of one 90° bend, in L/d
R_b = bend resistance due to one 90° bend, in L/d.

111

Example: Determine the equivalent lengths in pipe diameters of a 90° bend and a 270° bend having a relative radius of 12.

Solution: Referring to the *Total Resistance* curve, the equivalent length for a 90° bend is 34.5 pipe diameters.
The equivalent length of a 270° bend is

$$L/d = 34.5 + (3 - 1)[18.7 + (15.8 \div 2)]$$
$$= 87.7 \text{ pipe diameters.}$$

NOTE: This loss is less than the sum of losses through three 90° bends separated by tangents.

† From *Pressure Losses for Fluids in 90 Degree Pipe Bends* by K. H. Beij. Courtesy of Journal of Research of National Bureau of Standards, Vol. 21, July, 1938.
* Reproduced from Technical Paper #410, *Flow of Fluids*, Courtesy of Crane Co.

RESISTANCE TO MITER BENDS

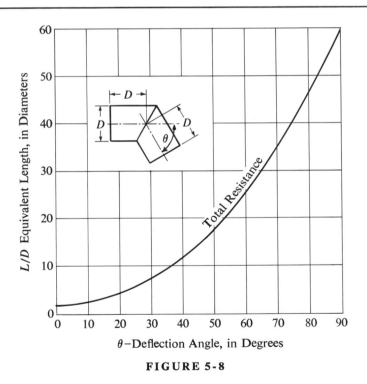

FIGURE 5-8

The chart above shows the resistance of miter bends to the flow of fluids. The chart is based on data published by the American Society of Mechanical Engineers (ASME).

Example: Determine the equivalent length in pipe diameters of a 40° miter bend.

Solution: Referring to the *Total Resistance* curve in the chart, the equivalent length is 12 pipe diameters.

TABLE 6

RESISTANCE DUE TO PIPE ENTRANCE AND EXIT*

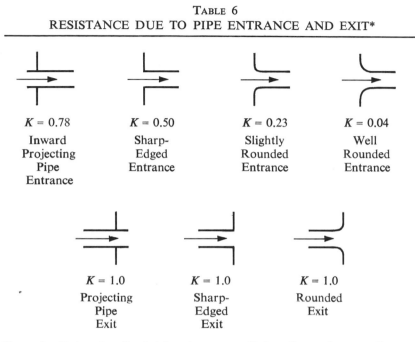

$K = 0.78$	$K = 0.50$	$K = 0.23$	$K = 0.04$
Inward Projecting Pipe Entrance	Sharp-Edged Entrance	Slightly Rounded Entrance	Well Rounded Entrance

$K = 1.0$	$K = 1.0$	$K = 1.0$
Projecting Pipe Exit	Sharp-Edged Exit	Rounded Exit

Example. Determine the total resistance coefficient for a pipe one diameter long having a sharp-edged entrance and a sharp-edged exit.

Solution: The resistance of pipe one diameter long is small and can be neglected ($K = fL/d$).

NOTE:

Resistance for a sharp-edged entrance = 0.5.
Resistance for a sharp-edged exit = 1.0.

Then,

the total resistance, K, for the pipe = 1.5.

* Reproduced from Technical Paper #410, *Flow of Fluids*, Courtesy of Crane Co.

reduction in pipe size takes place. The loss of head in terms of equivalent length of pipe is customarily used for pipe fittings. Table 5 and Figs. 5-7 and 5-8 indicate some of those losses.

Minor losses are often disregarded when they constitute a small fraction of the major pipe friction loss. For example, if a pipe is only 20 ft long, minor losses might be a large proportion of the total head loss; while if a pipe is 2000 feet long, it may be possible to neglect minor losses without serious error. To simplify the· solution of problems in this text, minor losses will be considered only when the value of L/d for each length of pipe in the system under consideration is greater than 1000.

The loss of head at the sharp-cornered pipe entrance from a large reservoir is $0.5(v^2/2g)$, and the loss at the outlet into a large reservoir is $1.0(v^2/2g)$. Table 6 indicates some additional minor losses at pipe entrances and exits.

5-6 HYDRAULIC AND ENERGY GRADIENTS

Because of the frictional resistance to flow in a flowing fluid, the pressure in a closed pipe will drop in the direction of flow. *When the variations in average pressure head along a pipe are plotted as ordinates from the center of the pipe, the line joining these points is called the hydraulic gradient, or hydraulic grade line. When the sums of the pressure head and velocity head at various sections of a pipe are plotted, the line joining these points is called the energy gradient.* Figure 5-9 indicates the hydraulic and energy gradients for a pipe line joining two reservoirs. The hydraulic gradient joins the points representing the sums of the pressure head and the elevation head taken with respect to a common reference plane as low or lower than any point on the pipe line.

At the entrance to the pipe in Fig. 5-9, the hydraulic gradient drops sharply due to the entrance loss and also due to the conversion of some of the pressure head into velocity head. The loss per unit of length of pipe due to flow through the pipe is constant so that the gradient slopes downward at a uniform rate. Again, at the outlet into the lower reservoir, the velocity head is lost. The energy gradient remains at a constant height above the hydraulic gradient since the diameter of the pipe does not change and thus the velocity head remains constant throughout the pipe

The hydraulic gradient indicates the pressure in a pipe line at any section of the pipe. When the gradient crosses or drops below the pipe line, it shows that the pressure in the pipe line becomes negative creating a vacuum in the line. Vacuums in a pipe line are generally to be avoided as they tend to promote the accumulation of air pockets at high points in the line, thereby retarding, and in some cases entirely stopping, the flow of the liquid. Plotting of the hydraulic gradient indicates those points along the pipe line where the pressure drops to zero. Pumps may be installed at such points to increase the pressure head and thereby maintain the desired flow.

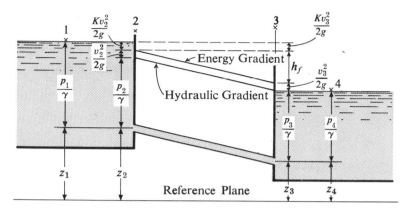

FIGURE 5-9

Example 5-6. Water ($\rho/\mu = 51{,}700$) flows from a reservoir to a tank that is 50 ft below the level of the reservoir. The water flows through 600 ft of 12-in. wrought iron pipe. Both ends of the pipe are sharp-cornered and submerged. Determine the discharge.

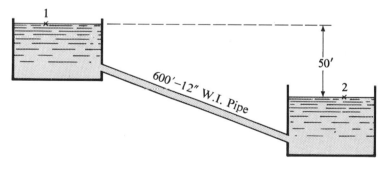

FIGURE 5-10

Solution: Figure 5-10 indicates the arrangement of the hydraulic system. Since L/d is less than 1000, minor losses should be considered. The Bernoulli equation becomes,

$$\frac{p_1}{\gamma} + z_1 + \frac{v_1^2}{2g} = \frac{p_2}{\gamma} + z_2 + \frac{v_2^2}{2g} + h_f + h_e + h_x$$

where $h_e = 0.5(v^2/2g)$, the entrance loss, and
$h_x = 1.0(v^2/2g)$, the exit loss.

Substituting known values

$$0 + 50 + 0 = 0 + 0 + 0 + f\frac{L}{d}\frac{v^2}{2g} + 0.5\frac{v^2}{2g} + 1.0\frac{v^2}{2g}$$

$$N_r = \frac{\rho v d}{\mu} = 51{,}000v(1)$$

and

$$\frac{K}{d} = \frac{0.0017}{12} = 0.000142.$$

Since N_r is unknown, assume $f = 0.020$.
Then,

$$50 = 0.020\frac{600}{1}\frac{v^2}{64.4} + 1.5\frac{v^2}{64.4} = 13.5\frac{v^2}{64.4}$$

and

$$v = \left[\frac{64.4(50)}{13.5}\right]^{1/2} = \left(\frac{3220}{13.5}\right)^{1/2} = 15.44 \text{ fps.}$$

Check: $N_r = 51{,}700(15.44) = 800{,}000$

$f = 0.0143.$

A second trial is necessary since f was assumed as 0.020.
Assume $f = 0.0143$, then

$$50 = (8.6 \overset{\bullet}{+} 1.5)\frac{v^2}{64.4}$$

and

$$v = \left(\frac{3220}{10.1}\right)^{1/2} = 17.86.$$

Check: $N_r = 51{,}700(17.86) = 923{,}000$

$f = 0.0143,$

which is the same as the assumed value. Therefore,

$$Q = av = \frac{\pi}{4}(17.86) = 14.0 \text{ cfs.}$$

Example 5-7.   Oil [$\rho = 1.75$ slugs/cu ft; $\mu = 550(10^{-6})$ slugs/ft-sec] is to be pumped from a reservoir into a tank car, as shown in Fig. 5-11. If the discharge is 1.5 cfs, determine the horsepower required if the pumping unit has an efficiency of 75 percent and all connections are sharp-cornered. ($K = 0.010$.)

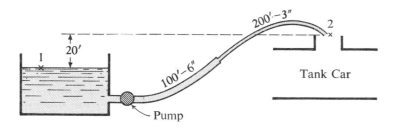

FIGURE 5-11

Solution: Computation of f for the 6-in. pipe:

$$v = \frac{Q}{a} = \frac{1.5(16)}{3.14} = 7.64 \text{ fps}$$

$$\frac{K}{d} = \frac{0.0100}{6} = 0.0017$$

$$N_r = \frac{\rho v d}{\mu} = 1.75(7.64)\tfrac{1}{2}\,\frac{10^6}{550} = 12{,}150$$

and, from the Moody diagram, $f = 0.032$.
Computation of f for the 3-in. pipe:

$$v = \frac{Q}{a} = 1.5\,\frac{64}{3.14} = 30.56 \text{ fps}$$

$$\frac{K}{d} = \frac{0.0100}{3} = 0.0033$$

$$N_r = \frac{\rho v d}{\mu} = 1.75(30.56)\tfrac{1}{4}\,\frac{10^6}{550} = 24{,}300$$

and, from the Moody diagram, $f = 0.0314$.
The minor losses are:

Loss from the reservoir into the 6-in. pipe = $0.5(v^2/2g)$.
The loss due to sudden contraction from 6-in. to 3-in. pipe = $0.33(v^2/2g)$.

The general Bernoulli equation is

$$\frac{p_1}{\gamma} + z_1 + \frac{v_1^2}{2g} + h_a = \frac{p_2}{\gamma} + z_2 + \frac{v_2^2}{2g} + h_e + h_f + h_c + h_f.$$

Substituting known values,

$$0 + 0 + 0 + h_a = 0 + 20 + \frac{30.56^2}{64.4} + 0.5\frac{7.64^2}{64.4}$$

$$+ 0.032(200)\frac{7.64^2}{64.4} + 0.33\frac{30.56^2}{64.4} + 0.0314(800)\frac{30.56^2}{64.4}$$

$$h_a = 20 + 14.51 + 0.45 + 5.80 + 4.79 + 364.28 = 409.83 \text{ ft}$$

$$\text{hp(output)} = \frac{Q\gamma h_a}{550} = \frac{1.5(1.75)32.2(409.83)}{550} = 62.98$$

$$\text{hp(input)} = \frac{62.98}{0.75} = 83.97 \text{ horsepower.}$$

Example 5-8. A horizontal 6-in. asphalted cast iron pipe discharges water $(\rho/\mu = 51,700)$ at the rate of 1.57 cfs from a reservoir, as shown in Fig. 5-12. At what distance from the reservoir will a pump in the pipe line become necessary to prevent a vacuum in the pipe?

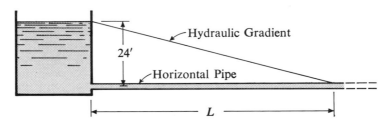

24'

Hydraulic Gradient

Horizontal Pipe

L

FIGURE 5-12

Solution:

$$v = \frac{Q}{a} = 1.57\frac{16}{3.14} = 8 \text{ fps}$$

$$\frac{K}{d} = \frac{0.005}{6} = 0.00083$$

$$N_r = 51,700(8)\tfrac{1}{2} = 206,800$$

and, from the Moody diagram, $f = 0.0203$.

Substituting known values into the Bernoulli equation, gives,

$$0 + 24 + 0 = 0 + 0 + \frac{8^2}{64.4} + 0.0203 \frac{L8^2}{\frac{1}{2}(64.4)} + 0.5 \frac{8^2}{64.4}$$

$$24 = 0.99 + 0.0403L + 0.50$$

$$L = \frac{22.51}{0.0403} = 558 \text{ ft.}$$

PROBLEMS

5-43. Water at 59°F is pumped at the rate of 1.57 cfs from a reservoir into a tank through 300 ft of 6-in. cast iron pipe (not including bends) as shown in Fig. P 5-43. Determine the total head loss. Relative radius of bends is 8.0.

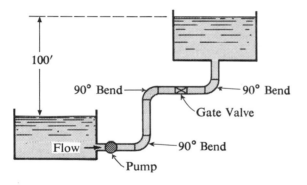

100′

90° Bend

Gate Valve

90° Bend

90° Bend

Flow

Pump

FIGURE P 5-43

5-44. For Prob. 5-43, determine the horsepower required.

5-45. Water at 32°F is to flow at the rate of 1.4 cfs from a reservoir into a lower tank. The water flows through 200 ft of 6-in. and 200 ft of 8-in. cast iron pipe. The pipe is connected in series. Determine the required difference in elevation of the water surfaces in the reservoir and in the tank. All connections are sharp-cornered.

5-46. Water flows from a reservoir through 100 ft of 6-in. and 200-ft of 12-in. steel pipe and discharges into the air at the point 40 ft below the water surface in the reservoir, as shown in Fig. P 5-46. The pipe is connected in series. Determine the discharge. All connections are sharp-cornered.

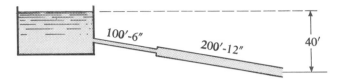

FIGURE P 5-46

5-47. Water flows from a reservoir through 100 ft of 12-in. wrought iron pipe that is connected in series with 50 ft of 6-in. wrought iron pipe that discharges into the air. Determine the vertical distance from the water surface in the reservoir to the discharge end of the 6-in. pipe when the discharge is 2.56 cfs. All connections are sharp-cornered.

5-48. Water at 32°F is to be discharged into a reservoir through 200 ft of 4-in. and 300 ft of 6-in. horizontal new steel pipe at the rate of 1.36 cfs. The pipe is connected in series. The 6-in. pipe discharges into the bottom of the reservoir, which is 12 ft below the water surface in the reservoir, as shown in Fig. P 5-48. What minimum pressure is required at the beginning of the 4-in. pipe?

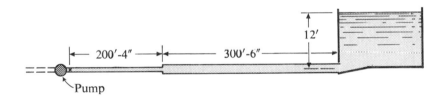

FIGURE P 5-48

5-49. Two tanks are connected by 200 ft of straight 12-in.-diameter wrought iron pipe containing two 90° bends, each with 6 ft radius. The water surface of one tank is 15 ft above the surface of the other tank. Determine the discharge.

5-50. Two tanks are to be connected by 250 ft of straight 12-in.-diameter wrought iron pipe containing three 90° standard elbows. What difference in elevation of the water surfaces in the two tanks is needed to maintain a discharge of 3.14 cfs?

5-51. What length of straight 3-in.-diameter pipe will produce the same head loss as two 3-in. standard ells when both pipe systems carry water at 68°F with a velocity of 8 fps?

5-52. How much friction head loss may be saved by replacing two 4-in., 90° long-radius ells, connected by 4 ft of straight pipe carrying water, with a length of 4-in. pipe, bent 180° to a 3-ft radius and having the same discharge. The velocity in the 4-in. pipe is 6 fps? $K = 0.006$.

5-53. If the head loss in a 4-in. gate valve is the same as that in 4.33 ft of straight 4-in. cast iron pipe when carrying water with a velocity of 12 fps at 59°F, what is the minor loss coefficient K for the valve?

5-7 DIVIDED FLOW

In many pipe systems, such as municipal water and sewerage systems, the pipes are so arranged that the flow from one point in the system to another point may take several paths, as indicated in Fig. 5-13.

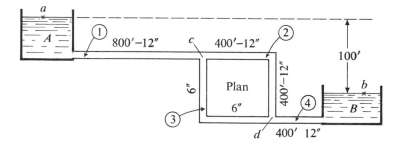

FIGURE 5-13

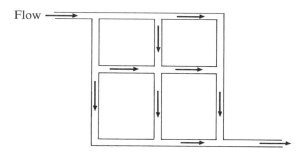

FIGURE 5-14

To demonstrate the method of solution for divided flow, a single 6-in.-diameter pipe branch will be added to the 12-in.-diameter pipe, connecting reservoirs A and B, as shown in Fig. 5-14. The 6-in. branch will be connected at points c and d. Water at 59°F flows from reservoir A into reservoir B, which is 100 feet below reservoir A.

Generally in the solution of divided flow problems, three steps should be followed:

1. Write the Bernoulli equation between the joints for each branch of pipe. The pressure at a joint will be the same for each pipe entering that joint, which means that the head loss in each branch will be the same.
2. Write all possible equations of continuity.
3. Solve the equations simultaneously. Where the diameter of a pipe or the discharge is unknown, the necessary assumptions and corrections for the friction value, f, must be made.

The Bernoulli equation for the two branches cd are:

For the 12-in. pipe, labelled number 2,

$$\frac{p_c}{\gamma} + \frac{v_2^2}{2g} + z_c = \frac{p_d}{\gamma} + \frac{v_2^2}{2g} + z_d + f_2(800)\frac{v_2^2}{2g} \tag{5-4}$$

and for the 6-in. pipe, labelled number 3,

$$\frac{p_c}{\gamma} + \frac{v_3^2}{2g} + z_c = \frac{p_d}{\gamma} + \frac{v_3^2}{2g} + z_d + f_3(1600)\frac{v_3^2}{2g}. \tag{5-5}$$

Equation (5.4) may be written

$$\frac{p_c}{\gamma} + z_c - \frac{p_d}{\gamma} - z_d = 800f_2\frac{v_2^2}{2g}$$

and Eq. (5-5) may be written,

$$\frac{p_c}{\gamma} + z_c - \frac{p_d}{\gamma} - z_d = 1600f_3\frac{v_3^2}{2g}.$$

Therefore,

$$800f_2v_2^2 = 1600f_3v_3^2$$

and

$$f_2v_2^2 = 2f_3v_3^2. \tag{5-6}$$

Now, writing the Bernoulli equation from point a to point b, through the 12-in. branch, gives,

$$0 + 100 + 0 = 0 + 0 + 0 + f_1800\frac{v_1^2}{2g} + f_2800\frac{v_2^2}{2g} + f_4400\frac{v_4^2}{2g}.$$

Since $v_1 = v_4$, and $f_1 = f_4$,

$$100 = 1200f_1 \frac{v_1^2}{2g} + 800f_2 \frac{v_2^2}{2g}. \tag{5-7}$$

Assuming all values of f equal to 0.02, Eq (5-6) becomes,

$$0.02v_2^2 = 0.04v_3^2$$

or

$$v_3 = \left(\frac{v_2^2}{2}\right)^{1/2} \tag{5-8}$$

and Eq. (5-7) becomes,

$$64.4 = 0.24v_1^2 + 0.16v_2^2$$

or

$$402.5 = 1.5v_1^2 + v_2^2. \tag{5-9}$$

From the equations of continuity,

$$Q_1 = Q_2 + Q_3,$$

and

$$a_1v_1 = a_2v_2 + a_3v_3.$$

However,

$$a_1 = a_2 \quad \text{and} \quad a_1 = 4a_3.$$

Therefore,

$$a_1v_1 = a_1v_2 + \frac{a_1v_3}{4}$$

so that

$$v_1 = v_2 + \frac{v_3}{4}. \tag{5-10}$$

Therefore, substituting the value of v_3 in Eq. (5-8) into Eq. (5-10), gives,

$$v_1 = v_2 + \frac{1}{4}\left(\frac{v_2^2}{2}\right)^{1/2}$$

so that

$$v_1 = 1.177v_2,$$

and

$$v_1^2 = 1.385v_2^2.$$

Substituting this value of v_1^2 into Eq. (5-9), gives,

$$402.5 = 1.5(1.385)v_2^2 + v_2^2 = 3.08v_2^2.$$

Therefore,

$$v_2 = 11.4 \text{ fps,}$$

and

$$v_1 = 1.177(11.4) = 13.42 \text{ fps.}$$

From Eq. (5-9),

$$v_3 = 4(13.42 - 11.40) = 8.08 \text{ fps.}$$

The velocities computed above are based on an assumed value of f of 0.02. This value of f must be checked by calculating the Reynolds number for each section of the pipe system, as follows:

$$R_1 = \frac{1.937(13.42)10^6}{23.83} = 1{,}090{,}000, \quad \text{and} \quad \frac{K}{d} = \frac{0.010}{12} = 0.00083,$$

for which $f_1 = 0.0191$.

$$R_2 = \frac{1.937(11.40)10^6}{23.83} = 926{,}000,$$

for which $f_2 = 0.0191$.

$$R_3 = \frac{1.937(8.08)10^6}{23.83} = 657{,}500, \quad \text{and} \quad \frac{K}{d} = \frac{0.0100}{6} = 0.0017,$$

for which $f_3 = 0.0228$.

The f for the 6-in.-diameter pipe varies more than 10 percent from the assumed value of f. Using the new values of f, Eq. (5-6) becomes,

$$0.0191v_2^2 = 0.0456v_3^2,$$

and

$$v_3 = \left(\frac{v_2^2}{2.39}\right)^{1/2} \tag{5-11}$$

Also, Eq. (5-9) becomes,

$$64.4 = 0.229v_1^2 + 0.1526v_2^2,$$

and

$$422 = 1.5v_1^2 + v_2^2. \tag{5-12}$$

The equations of continuity do not change. Again, substituting the value of v_3 in Eq. (5-11) into Eq. (5-10), gives,

$$v_1 = v_2 + \frac{1}{4}\left(\frac{v_2^2}{2.39}\right)^{1/2} = 1.162v_2$$

and

$$v_1^2 = 1.35v_2^2.$$

Substituting the value of v_1^2 into Eq. (5-12), gives,

$$422 = 1.5(1.35)v_2^2 + v_2^2 = 3.025v_2^2,$$

and

$$v_2^2 = 139.5.$$

Therefore,

$$v_2 = 11.81 \text{ fps,}$$

$$v_1 = 1.162(11.81) = 13.72 \text{ fps,}$$

and

$$v_3 = 4(13.72 - 11.81) = 7.64 \text{ fps.}$$

Again, checking the values of f,

$$R_1 = \frac{1.937(13.72)10^6}{23.83} = 1,115,000,$$

for which $f = 0.0191$.

$$R_2 = \frac{1.937(11.81)10^6}{23.83} = 960,000,$$

for which $f = 0.0191$.

$$R_3 = \frac{1.937(7.64)10^6}{23.83} = 620,000,$$

for which $f = 0.0228$. All values check with the previously used values of f. Therefore, the discharges are as follows:

Through the 12-in. branch, $\frac{\pi}{4}11.81 = 9.28$ cfs

Through the 6-in. branch, $\frac{\pi}{4}7.64 = 1.50$ cfs

Through the main line, $\frac{\pi}{4}13.72 = 10.78$ cfs,

which checks the discharge through the two branches.

As the pipe system adds branches and becomes more complicated, the solution involves more and more equations that require simultaneous solutions. In such situations, special methods, which are not covered in this text, are employed to simplify such solutions.

PROBLEMS

5-54. The discharge through the 6-in.-diameter wrought iron pipe loop, shown in Fig. P 5-54, is 3 cfs of water at 32°F. Determine the discharge through each branch of the loop.

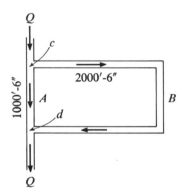

FIGURE P 5-54

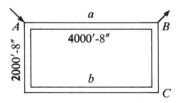

FIGURE P 5-56

5-55. Solve Prob. 5-54, if a 12-in.-diameter wrought iron pipe is used for branch *B*.

5-56. A loop of horizontal 8-in.-diameter new cast iron pipe, as shown in Fig. P 5-56, carries 4 cfs of water from point *A* to point *B*. Determine the discharge through each branch of the loop.

5-57. Solve Prob. 5-56, if the discharge end is located at point *C* instead of point *B*, and one of the branches is changed to a 12-in.-diameter pipe.

Chapter *6*

Flow Measuring Devices in Closed Pipes

6-1 VENTURI METER

One of the more commonly used methods of measuring the flow of fluids in closed conduits is by means of the *venturi meter*, invented by Herschel.[1] This device is shown in Fig. 6-1, and consists essentially of a rather short converging section of pipe that directs the flow of the fluid into a much longer diverging section. The longer diverging section is necessary to dampen out turbulence as the flow expands into the larger diameter pipe. A manometer or other pressure measuring device is attached to the inlet and the throat of the meter. As the fluid flows from the inlet through the throat the pressure decreases and the velocity increases. The pressure difference is measured and the relative velocities determined from the diameters of the inlet and throat of the meter by the application of the equation of continuity, $a_1v_1 = a_2v_2$, where a_1 is the area of the inlet and a_2 is the area of the throat of the venturi meter.

Since the loss of head in a venturi meter is small, it is placed directly

---

1. Herschel, Clemens, "The Venturi Meter," *Trans. Am. Soc. Civil Eng.* **XVII**, 228 (1887).

in the flow line. Generally, the *meter coefficient, which is the ratio of the actual discharge to the discharge measured without loss of head (ideal discharge) through the meter, is approximately 0.98.*

The following examples illustrate the procedure used in measuring flow in a closed pipe.

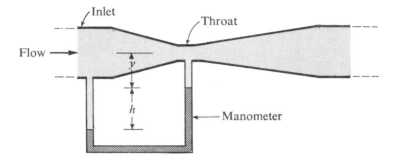

FIGURE 6-1

Example 6-1. If a differential mercury manometer, attached to the inlet and throat of a 6-in. by 3-in. horizontal venturi meter, indicates a reading of 18 in., determine **(a)** the ideal discharge of water through the 6-in. pipe, and **(b)** the actual discharge. Assume a meter coefficient of 0.97.

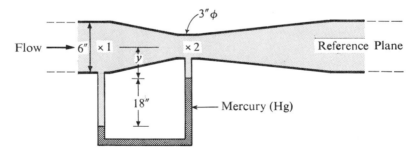

FIGURE 6-2

Solution: Figure 6-2 shows the venturi meter in the 6-in. pipe line and the mercury manometer attached to the inlet and throat of the meter. Points 1 and 2 are taken at the center of the inlet and throat of the meter, respectively. Also, the reference plane is taken at the centroidal longitudinal axis of the pipe.

Writing the manometer equation in terms of feet of water, gives

$$\frac{p_1}{\gamma} + y + 1.5 - 13.6(1.5) - y = \frac{p_2}{\gamma}.$$

Therefore,

$$\frac{p_1 - p_2}{\gamma} = 12.6(1.5) = 18.9 \text{ ft of water.} \tag{6-1}$$

Also, by the Bernoulli equation, assuming no loss,

$$\frac{p_1 - p_2}{\gamma} = \frac{v_2^2 - v_1^2}{64.4}. \tag{6-2}$$

Since the velocities are inversely proportional to each other as the square of the diameters,

$$\frac{v_1}{v_2} = \frac{3^2}{6^2} = \frac{1}{4}.$$

Therefore,

$$v_2 = 4v_1 \qquad \text{and} \qquad v_2^2 = 16v_1^2.$$

Substituting the value of $(p_1 - p_2)/\gamma$, from Eq. (6-1), into Eq. (6-2), gives,

$$18.9 = \frac{16v_1^2 - v_1^2}{64.4} = \frac{15v_1^2}{64.4}.$$

Therefore,

$$v_1 = \left[\frac{64.4(18.9)}{15}\right]^{1/2} = 9.0 \text{ fps,}$$

and

$$Q = \frac{\pi}{16}(9.0) = 1.77 \text{ cfs.}$$

(b) Since the meter coefficient is the ratio of the actual discharge (or velocity) at a cross section of the pipe to the ideal discharge (or velocity) at that cross section, that is $C = Q_{act'l}/Q_{ideal}$, therefore,

$$0.97 = \frac{Q_{act'l}}{1.77}$$

and

$$Q_{act'l} = 1.77(0.97) = 1.71 \text{ cfs.}$$

PROBLEMS

6-1.   Determine the ideal discharge of water through a 12-in. by 6-in. venturi meter when the differential mercury manometer, attached to the inlet and throat of the meter, shows a reading of 26 inches.

6-2.   Determine the differential mercury reading on a manometer, attached to a 12-in. by 6-in. venturi meter, which discharges 5 cfs of water. The head loss between the inlet and throat of the meter is 3 ft of water.

6-3.   For Prob. 6-2, determine the meter coefficient.

6-4.   A 16-in. by 8-in. venturi meter is placed in a pipe line carrying 15 cfs of crude oil "B" at 60°F. If the meter coefficient is 0.97 and a pressure gage at the throat reads 10 psi, determine the pressure at the inlet.

6-5.   A 4-in. by 2-in. venturi meter has a coefficient of 0.96 when the differential mercury manometer reading is 20 in. If castor oil at 68°F is flowing through the meter, determine the head loss between the inlet and the throat.

6-6.   A mercury manometer, which has a maximum differential reading of 48 in., is used with a 24-in. by 12-in. venturi meter. The venturi meter is installed in a water line. If the pressure lost between inlet and throat is 3 psi, determine the maximum discharge that can be measured.

6-7.   A venturi meter is to be placed in an 8-in. pipe line carrying water. If the maximum discharge is 3.14 cfs, and the mercury manometer has a maximum differential height of 24-in., determine the minimum permissible throat diameter. Assume the friction loss between inlet and throat at 20 percent of the velocity head at the throat.

6-8.   A 6-in. by 4-in. venturi meter, installed in a pipe line, carries gasoline "A" at 60°F. Determine the discharge when the differential water manometer, attached to the meter, reads 9 inches. The friction loss between inlet and throat of the meter is equal to 8 percent of the velocity head at the throat.

6-9.   A 6-in. by 2-in. venturi meter discharges glycerine at 100°F at the rate of 2400 lb/minute. A pressure gage at the inlet reads 18 psi and a gage at the throat reads 10 psi. Determine the frictional head loss between the inlet and the throat.

6-10. Oxygen at 32°F passes through a 4-in. by 2-in. venturi meter. Determine the discharge when a manometer, containing water at 32°F, attached to the inlet and throat, indicates a differential reading of 2 inches. The gage pressure at the inlet is 2 psi. Neglect friction and any change in the density of the oxygen.

6-11. Air at 59°F is passed through a 3-in. by 1-in. venturi meter. The velocity at the throat is 40 fps and the gage pressure at the throat is 0.46 psi. Determine the differential reading on a water manometer attached to the meter. Neglect friction and any change in density of the air.

6-12. Helium at 32°F is passed through a 2-in. by 1-in. venturi meter that has a meter coefficient of 0.98. When the pressure gage at the inlet reads 18 psi and the gate at the throat reads 17.9 psi, determine the discharge.

6-13. A 4-in. by 2-in. venturi meter is installed in a 4-in. pipe line carrying carbon tetrachloride ($S_g = 1.60$). The discharge is 0.570 cfs when a mercury manometer attached to the inlet and throat has a differential reading of 18 inches. Determine the meter coefficient.

6-14. A 4-in. by 2-in. venturi meter is placed in an oil line ($S_g = 0.80$). When the mercury manometer, attached to inlet and throat, indicates a differential reading of 15 in., the discharge is 2270 lb/minute. Determine the meter coefficient.

6-15. Oil ($S_g = 0.80$) is flowing through the 6-in. by 2-in. venturi meter, as shown in Fig. P 6-15. The meter coefficient is 0.95. Determine the discharge.

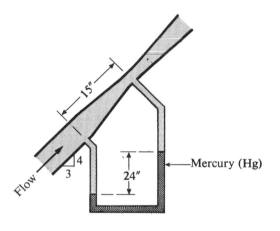

FIGURE P 6-15

6-2 NOZZLES

A nozzle is a converging tube attached to the end of a hose or a pipe. By constricting the area of flow, the velocity of the jet is greatly increased. Figure 6-3 shows two types of nozzles. In Fig. 6-3(a) the tip of the nozzle is formed so that the stream does not converge after leaving the tip. In Fig. 6-3(b) the jet converges to what is known as the *vena contracta*. At the point of convergence, the pressure becomes essentially zero gage and the cross-sectional area of the jet is minimum. Since a nozzle resembles the converging portion of the venturi meter, *the coefficient of velocity, which is the ratio of the actual velocity to the ideal velocity without friction loss,* approximates, in many instances, the meter coefficient of 0.98. For the type of nozzle that has a vena contracta beyond the tip of the nozzle, *the ratio of the area of the vena contracta to the area of the tip of the nozzle is called the coefficient of contraction.* The following examples illustrate these concepts.

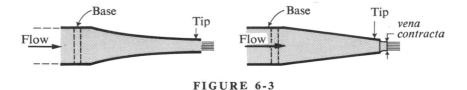

FIGURE 6-3

Example 6-2.   A 6-in. by 2-in. nozzle, similar to that shown in Fig. 6-3(a), is attached to the end of a 6-in. pipe. The pressure at the base of the nozzle (where it joins the pipe) is 60 psi and the coefficient of velocity, C_v, is 0.98. Determine the velocity of the jet.

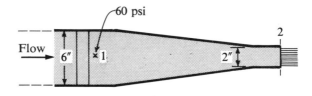

FIGURE 6-4

Solution: Figure 6-4 shows the nozzle attached to the 6-in. pipe. Writing the Bernoulli equation from point 1 to point 2 to determine the ideal velocity gives,

$$\frac{60}{0.433} + 0 + \frac{v_1^2}{64.4} = 0 + 0 + \frac{v_2^2}{64.4}.$$

Also,

$$\frac{v_1}{v_2} = \frac{4}{36} = \frac{1}{9}.$$

Therefore,

$$v_2 = 9v_1 \quad \text{and} \quad v_2^2 = 81v_1^2.$$

Substituting these values into the Bernoulli equation gives

$$\frac{60}{0.433} = \frac{81v_1^2 - v_1^2}{64.4} = \frac{80v_1^2}{64.4}.$$

Therefore,

$$v_1 = \left[\frac{64.4(60)}{80(0.433)} \right]^{1/2} = 10.55 \text{ fps (ideal velocity).}$$

Since

$$\frac{v_{\text{act'l}}}{v_{\text{ideal}}} = 0.98, \qquad v_{\text{act'l}} = 0.98(10.55) = 10.34 \text{ fps,}$$

and

v_2 (the velocity of the jet) $= 9v_1 = 9(10.34) = 93.1$ fps.

Example 6-3. A 4-in. by 1-in. nozzle, similar to that shown in Fig. 6-3(b), is attached to the end of a 4-in. hose line. The velocity of the water leaving the nozzles is 96 fps, the coefficient of velocity, C_v, is 0.96 and the coefficient of contraction, C_c, is 0.80. Determine the necessary pressure at the base of the nozzle.

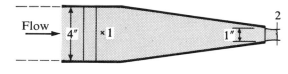

FIGURE 6-5

Solution: Figure 6-5 shows the nozzle attached to the 4-in. hose line. Since the coefficient of velocity, C_v, is $v_{\text{act'l}}/v_{\text{ideal}}$;

$$v_{\text{ideal}} = \frac{96}{0.96} = 100 \text{ fps.}$$

Also, since

$$\frac{v_1}{v_2} = \frac{a_2}{a_1} = \frac{d_2^2}{d_1^2} = 0.8 \frac{(1)^2}{4^2} = \frac{1}{20},$$

$$v_1 = \frac{100}{20} = 5 \text{ fps (ideal).}$$

Substituting these values into the Bernoulli equation, gives

$$\frac{p_1}{0.433} + 0 + \frac{5^2}{64.4} = 0 + 0 + \frac{100^2}{64.4}$$

and

$$\frac{p_1}{0.433} = \frac{10,000 - 25}{64.4} = \frac{9975}{64.4} = 155 \text{ ft.}$$

Therefore,

$$p_1 = 0.433(155) = 67.1 \text{ psi.}$$

PROBLEMS

6-16. Determine the pressure in psi necessary at the base of a 1-in. by ½-in. nozzle, for which C_v is 0.98 and C_c is 1.00, to discharge water at the rate of 0.20 cfs.

6-17. Determine the pressure required at the base of the nozzle in Prob. 6-16, if C_c is 0.90.

6-18. A 3-in. by 1-in. nozzle, for which C_v is 0.96 and C_c is 0.90, is attached to the end of a fire hose. If the water leaves the nozzle with a velocity of 80 fps, determine the pressure at the inlet to the nozzle.

6-19. A 3-in. by 1-in. nozzle, for which C_v is 0.94 and C_c is 0.90, has a pressure at its base of 80 psi. Determine **(a)** the velocity of the water at the tip of the nozzle, and **(b)** the head loss in the nozzle.

6-20. A 4-in. by 2-in. nozzle, for which C_v is 0.90 and C_c is 0.80, is discharging 1.57 cfs of water into the atmosphere. Determine **(a)** the pressure at the base of the nozzle, and **(b)** the head loss in the nozzle.

6-21. Water flows through a 2-in. by 1-in. nozzle, for which C_v is 0.96 and C_c is 0.90, and strikes a Pelton wheel with a velocity of 80 fps. Determine the pressure at the base of the nozzle.

6-22. Water flows through a 2-in. by 1-in. nozzle, for which C_v is 0.96 and C_c is 0.93, and strikes a Pelton wheel. If the pressure at the base of the nozzle is 43.3 psi, determine the velocity of the jet.

6-23. A 4-in. by 2-in. nozzle, for which C_v is 0.94 and C_c is 0.80, is discharging 0.57 cfs of water into the atmosphere. Determine **(a)** the pressure at the base of the nozzle, and **(b)** the head loss in the nozzle.

6-24. Determine the pressure at the base of a 3-in. by 1-in. nozzle, for which C_v is 0.94 and C_c is 0.90, when it is discharging 0.52 cfs of water.

6-25. Determine the pressure at the base of a 3-in. by 1-in. nozzle, for which C_v is 0.97 and C_c is 0.95, when it is discharging 0.50 cfs of water.

6-26. A pressure gage at the base of a 3-in. by 1-in. nozzle, for which C_v is 0.97 and C_c is 1.00, reads 60 psi. Determine the discharge of water through the nozzle.

6-27. A 3-in. by 1-in. nozzle is placed at the end of a 3-in. horizontal water pipe. C_v is 0.94 and C_c is 0.90. An open mercury manometer, attached to the base of the nozzle, indicates a differential reading of 18 inches, as shown in Fig. P 6-27. Determine the discharge in cfs.

6-28. A 3-in. by 1-in. nozzle, for which C_v is 0.95 and C_c is 0.90, is attached to a horizontal 3-in. pipe line discharging oil ($S_g = 0.80$) at the rate of 0.628 cfs. Determine the pressure at the base of the nozzle.

6-29. If C_c is 0.90 in Prob. 6-26, determine the discharge.

6-30. Solve Prob. 6-26. Assume that gasoline "B" at 60°F is being discharged, and C_v and C_c remain unchanged.

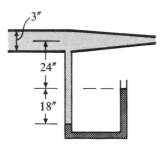

FIGURE P 6-27

6-3 ORIFICE METERS

In some instances, where space is limited and head loss is not important, an *orifice meter* is placed in a pipe line to measure fluid flow. The orifice meter consists of a flat plate with a hole, or flow nozzle, at its center. This flow nozzle is called an orifice and is clamped between two flanges, as shown in Fig. 6-6. As the fluid flows through the orifice, the velocity

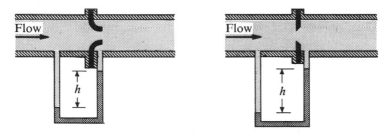

FIGURE 6-6

increases and the pressure drops. This is similar to the fluid flow through the throat of a venturi meter. However, the difference in velocity in the pipe and in the orifice is usually much greater in an orifice meter and the loss of head is, therefore, greater. The difference in pressure as the fluid passes through the orifice can be measured by pressure gages or by differential manometers, as indicated in Fig. 6-6. *The meter coefficient is the ratio of the actual discharge (or velocity) to the ideal discharge (or velocity) at any section.* The coefficient depends on the thickness of the orifice plate, the size of the opening relative to the size of the pipe, the shape of the opening, the fluid, and the location of the taps for the manometer. Each orifice plate should be calibrated to determine the correct coefficient. For sharp-edged flat plate orifice meters, the coefficient usually approximates 0.60.

When the orifice plate is placed at the end of a pipe the pressure at the discharged side of the plate is zero. The situation is similar to that of the nozzle with the converging stream at the tip. The area of the jet as it passes through the orifice becomes minimum at the vena contracta, where the pressure is approximately zero gage. However, the coefficient of velocity and coefficient of contraction will vary considerably since they depend on the relative size of the orifice and the pipe diameter, the shape of the edge of the orifice, the thickness of the orifice plate, and the nature of the fluid flowing.

The computation of the discharge of a fluid passing through the orifice meter is analogous to the computation used for the venturi meter, as illustrated by the following examples.

Example 6-4.   Water at 68°F flows through a 1-in.-diameter nozzle type orifice plate located in the center of a 4-in. pipe, as shown in Fig. 6-7. If the discharge is 0.38 cfs and the meter coefficient is 0.80, determine the probable differential mercury manometer reading in inches of mercury.

Solution: The ideal discharge is computed as follows:

$$Q_i = \frac{Q_a}{C} = \frac{0.38}{0.80} = 0.475 \text{ cfs.}$$

The ideal velocities v_1 and v_2 are

$$v_1 = \frac{Q}{a} = 0.475 \frac{36}{3.14} = 5.45 \text{ fps}$$

$$v_2 = 0.475 \frac{576}{3.14} = 87.2 \text{ fps.}$$

Substituting into the Bernoulli equation, gives

$$\frac{p_1 - p_2}{\gamma} = \frac{87.2^2 - 5.45^2}{64.4} = \frac{7556}{64.4} = 117.3 \text{ ft of water.}$$

The manometer equation is

$$\frac{p_1 - p_2}{\gamma} = \frac{13.6h}{12} - \frac{h}{12} = \frac{12.6h}{12}.$$

Therefore,

$$\frac{12.6h}{12} = 117.3,$$

and

$$h = \frac{12(117.3)}{12.6} = 111.7 \text{ inches of mercury.}$$

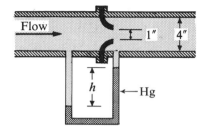

FIGURE 6-7

Example 6-5. Oxygen at 32°F flows from a storage tank through a ½-in.-diameter hole in an orifice plate that is inserted in a 2-in. pipe line. If the differential water manometer attached to the orifice meter indicates 3 in. of water, as shown in Fig. 6-8, determine the discharge in cfs. The meter coefficient is 0.60. Assume that the density and temperature of the oxygen remain constant.

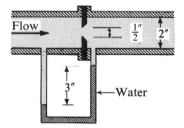

FIGURE 6-8

Solution: Oxygen at 32°F, from Table 1, weighs 0.08921 lb/cu ft. Writing the manometer equation from point 1 to point 2, in terms of pressure, gives,

$$p_1 + \frac{1}{4}\frac{(0.08921)}{144} - \frac{1}{4}(0.433) = p_2,$$

and

$$p_1 - p_2 - \frac{1}{4}(0.433 - 0.00062) = 0.1082,$$

so

$$\frac{p_1 - p_2}{\gamma} = \frac{0.1082(144)}{0.08921} = 174.7 \text{ ft of oxygen.}$$

Since

$$\frac{v_1}{v_2} = \frac{\frac{1}{2}^2}{2^2} = \frac{1}{16},$$

$$v_2^2 = 256v_1^2.$$

Substituting into the Bernoulli equation, gives

$$\frac{p_1 - p_2}{\gamma} = \frac{256v_1^2 - v_1^2}{64.4} = \frac{255v_1^2}{64.4}.$$

Therefore,

$$\frac{255v_1^2}{64.4} = 174.7,$$

and

$$v_1 = \left[\frac{174.7(64.4)}{255}\right]^{1/2} = 6.64 \text{ fps.}$$

The discharge, then, is

$$Q = \frac{\pi}{144}(6.64) = 0.145 \text{ cfs.}$$

Example 6-6. An orifice plate, which has a 1-in.-diameter orifice, is placed at the end of a 3-in. water line. The coefficient of velocity, C_v, is 0.94, and the coefficient of contraction, C_c, is 0.90. If the discharge is 0.52 cfs, determine the probable pressure near the end of the pipe.

FIGURE 6-9

Solution: Figure 6-9 is a sketch of the pipe and orifice plate. Since the discharge is given,

$$v_{1(\text{act'l})} = \frac{0.52(64)}{3.14} = 10.6 \text{ fps} \quad \text{and} \quad v_{1(\text{ideal})} = \frac{10.6}{0.94} = 11.27 \text{ fps.}$$

Also,

$$v_{2(\text{act'l})} = \frac{0.52(576)}{0.90(3.14)} = 106 \text{ fps} \quad \text{and} \quad v_{2(\text{ideal})} = \frac{106}{0.94} = 112.7 \text{ fps.}$$

Writing the Bernoulli equation from point 1 to point 2, gives

$$\frac{p_1}{0.433} + 0 + \frac{11.27^2}{64.4} = 0 + 0 + \frac{112.7^2}{64.4}$$

$$p_1 = \frac{(12,700 - 127)}{64.4}\, 0.433 = 84.5 \text{ psi.}$$

PROBLEMS

6-31. Determine the ideal discharge of water through a 6-in. by 3-in. orifice meter if the differential mercury manometer, attached to the meter, indicates a reading of 24 inches.

6-32. Determine the actual discharge for Prob. 6-31, if the meter coefficient is 0.63.

6-33. Determine the differential mercury reading on a manometer attached to a 6-in. by 3-in. orifice meter. The discharge is 1.37 cfs of water. Assume the head loss through the meter at 20 ft of water.

6-34. A 2-in. by 1-in. orifice meter has a coefficient of 0.60 when the differential mercury manometer reading is 24 inches. The oil passing through the meter weighs 50 pcf. Determine the head loss in the meter.

6-35. A 16-in. by 8-in. orifice meter is placed in a pipe line carrying 8 cfs of crude oil "B" at 60°F. If the meter coefficient is 0.65 and a pressure gage at the orifice reads 6 psi, determine the pressure at the inlet.

6-36. A 4-in. by 2-in. orifice meter has a coefficient of 0.60 when the differential mercury manometer reading is 20 inches. If castor oil at 68°F is flowing through the meter, determine the head loss.

6-37. A 4-in. by 2-in. orifice meter is installed in a 4-in. pipe line carrying carbon tetrachloride ($S_g = 1.60$). The discharge is 0.400 cfs when a mercury manometer attached to the meter has a differential reading of 18 inches. Determine the meter coefficient.

6-38. A 4-in. by 2-in. orifice meter is placed in an oil line ($S_g = 0.80$). When the mercury manometer attached to the meter indicates a differential reading of 30 inches, the discharge is 2150 lb/minute. Determine the meter coefficient.

6-39. A plate containing a 3-in.-diameter orifice is placed over the end of a 6-in. pipe carrying water. A pressure gage near the end of the pipe indicates a pressure of 35 psi. $C_v = 0.90$ and $C_c = 0.85$. Determine the discharge.

6-40. A plate containing a 2-in.-diameter orifice is placed over the end of a 6-in. pipe carrying water. If the diameter of the vena contracta is

1.52 in. and the discharge is 0.48 cfs when the pressure near the end of the pipe is 25 psi, determine (a) the coefficient of contraction, (b) the coefficient of velocity, and (c) the coefficient of discharge.

6-41. A plate containing a 1.50-in.-diameter orifice is fastened over the end of a 4-in. pipe carrying water. A pressure gage near the end of the pipe indicates a pressure of 30 psi. $C_v = 0.90$ and $C_c = 0.80$. Determine the discharge.

6-42. A plate containing a 3-in.-diameter orifice is fastened over the end of a 4-in. pipe. If the measured discharge is 1.00 cfs of water and the diameter of the vena contracta is 2.75 in. when the pressure near the end of the pipe is 5.0 psi, determine the coefficient of velocity.

6-4 PITOT TUBE

A device used for measuring the velocity of flow of a fluid, especially gases, is called the *pitot tube*. It consists of a tube placed in a stream of fluid with its axis in the direction of flow, as shown in Fig. 6-10. A stagnation point,

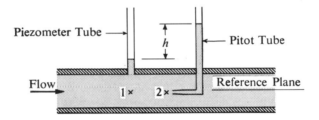

FIGURE 6-10

or point of zero velocity, occurs at point 2, a short distance in front of the end of the tube. A piezometer tube indicates the pressure in the fluid near the end of the pitot tube. Writing the Bernoulli equation from point 1 to point 2 and taking the reference plane through the center of the tube, gives

$$\frac{p_1}{\gamma} + 0 + \frac{v_1^2}{2g} = \frac{p_2}{\gamma} + 0 + 0$$

and

$$v_1 = \left[\frac{(p_2 - p_1)}{\gamma} 2g\right]^{1/2}.$$

Substituting the height, h, for the differential pressure head, $(p_2 - p_1)/\gamma$, gives

$$v_1 = (2gh)^{1/2}.$$

If the pressure at the streamline in which the pitot tube is located differs from the pressure indicated by the piezometer tube, a correction is necessary. Also, the design and placement of the tube in the fluid stream may alter the results so that a coefficient, C, is introduced in order to correct these factors. This gives the following equation,

$$v_1 = C(2gh)^{1/2} . \qquad (6\text{-}3)$$

A more convenient method used to determine the value of the differential pressure head, h, between points 1 and 2 is to connect these points with a differential manometer, as shown in Fig. 6-11. The resultant combination is known as a *pitot-static tube*. Most aircraft determine their airspeed by the use of some type of pitot tube.

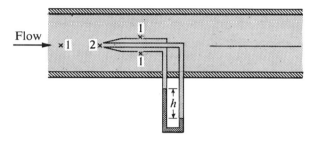

FIGURE 6-11

Example 6-7. A pitot-static tube, having a coefficient of 0.88, is mounted on an airplane. When the differential water manometer indicates a reading of 8 inches (air temperature 59°F), determine the probable relative velocity of the plane.

Solution: Equation (6-3), with $C = 0.88$, gives

$$v_1 = 0.88(2gh)^{1/2}.$$

Since v_1 is the velocity of the air with respect to the airplane, or vice versa, h must be converted into feet of air. Thus,

$$\frac{0.0765(h)}{144} = \frac{8}{12}(0.433),$$

and

$$h = \tfrac{2}{3}(0.433)144\,\frac{10^4}{765} = 543 \text{ ft of air.}$$

Therefore,
$$v_1 = 0.88[64.4(543)]^{1/2} = 164 \text{ fps}$$
or
$$v_1 = \frac{164(60)}{88} = 112 \text{ miles/hour.}$$

PROBLEMS

6-43. A pitot-static tube with a coefficient of 0.83 indicates a differential of 3 inches of water when held in a stream of air at 68°F. Determine the velocity of the air.

6-44. Determine the water differential required to indicate an airspeed, in air at 32°F, of 180 mph if the coefficient of the pitot-static tube is 0.80.

6-45. Air at 59°F flows by a pitot-static tube with a relative velocity of 60 mph. If the coefficient of the tube is 0.871 under these conditions, determine the water differential that would be obtained.

6-5 CAVITATION

Cavitation in a liquid occurs when the pressure in a pipe approaches absolute zero causing the formation of bubbles or vapor pockets due to the rapid vaporization of the liquid as it flows through a region that is at the vapor pressure of the liquid.

As observed for the venturi meter, when the velocity increases the pressure decreases. However, there is a minimum pressure below which the velocity cannot go. This point is the absolute zero pressure, or the vapor pressure, of the liquid. As the velocity is further increased the liquid will vaporize. This vaporization, or cavitation, can be structurally harmful to the pipe. As the vapor pockets reach areas of increased pressure they collapse with explosive force, causing vibrations and deterioration of the pipe due to the rapid oxidation of the inner surface of the pipe.

Example 6-8. Determine the maximum discharge of water at 32°F that may be carried by a 6-in. by 3-in. venturi meter, which has a coefficient of 0.95, without cavitation when the inlet pressure is 24 psia.

Solution: Since cavitation impends when the pressure at the throat of the venturi meter reaches vapor pressure, the absolute pressure head at the throat will be 0.204 ft of water (Table 1). The ideal velocity, under these conditions, can be determined by use of the Bernoulli equation, thus,

$$\frac{24}{0.433} + 0 + \frac{v_1^2}{64.4} = 0.204 + 0 + \frac{v_2^2}{64.4}.$$

Since $v_2 = 4v_1$,

$$v_2^2 = 16v_1^2,$$

and

$$\frac{15v_1^2}{64.4} = 55.5 - 0.2 = 55.3.$$

Therefore,

$$v_1 = \left[\frac{55.3(64.4)}{15}\right]^{1/2} = 15.4 \text{ fps (ideal)}$$

$$v_{1(\text{act'l})} = 0.95(15.4) = 14.6 \text{ fps.}$$

Thus,

$$Q_{\text{act'l}} = 14.6\frac{(3.14)}{16} = 2.87 \text{ cfs.}$$

PROBLEMS

6-46. A 1.4-in. by 0.70-in. venturi meter carries water at 59°F. The meter coefficient is 0.97 and the pressure at the inlet is 12 psig. At what differential mercury manometer reading would cavitation be expected?

6-47. A 2-in. by 1-in. venturi meter carries water at 68°F. The meter coefficient is 0.98, and the pressure at the inlet is 12 psi. Determine the discharge when cavitation is impending.

6-48. A 6-in. by 2-in. orifice is placed in a pipe line. The coefficient of the meter is 0.60 and the pressure at the inlet is 20 psi. Determine the discharge in cfs of water at 68°F when cavitation is impending.

6-6 SIPHONS

When designing pipe systems, it becomes necessary at times to run the pipe line around or over certain obstructions and this places a portion of the pipe higher than the source of flow, creating what is known as a *siphon*. Figure 6-12 indicates the flow of water from a reservoir through such a siphon. The distance, d, cannot be greater than the column of water supported by the atmospheric pressure minus the vapor pressure head. At sea level this is, ideally, approximately 34 ft. Due to vapor pressure and pipe friction this distance may be materially reduced. For this maximum height, the pressure at the summit of the siphon approaches zero absolute, or at sea level, -14.7 psi. Under this extreme vacuum, entrapped air in the water will tend to accumulate at the high point of the siphon, and when this accumulation of air becomes large enough it will stop the flow of the fluid in the pipe. To correct this condition, it is good practice to install a pump at the high point of the siphon. The pump will remove any accumulation of air.

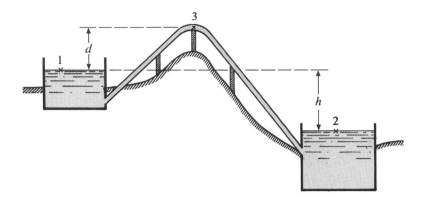

FIGURE 6-12

To insure continuous flow in a siphon at the desired rate, the following procedure should be followed:

1. Write the Bernoulli equation from point 1, the beginning of the system, to point 2, the discharge end, to determine the apparent velocity in the siphon. (See Fig. 6-12.)
2. Using the velocity found in step 1, write the Bernoulli equation from point 1 to point 3, the summit of the siphon, and solve for the pressure head at point 3.
3. If the pressure head, p_3/γ, at the summit is found to be equal to or greater than the least possible atmospheric pressure head plus the vapor pressure head, the velocity found under step 1 is valid.
4. If the pressure head, p_3/γ, at the summit is found to be less than the least possible atmospheric pressure head plus the vapor pressure head, the velocity found under step 1 is not valid.
5. When the velocity found under step 1 is found not to be valid, write the Bernoulli equation from point 1 to point 3, and solve for the velocity of the fluid at point 3 in the siphon. Assume the lowest possible pressure at the summit. The product of this velocity and the area of the pipe at point 3 is the correct discharge. In this case, if the discharge end of the pipe is not submerged, the pipe may not run full at the discharge end.

Example 6-9. Kerosene [$\gamma = 50.6$ pcf; $\mu = 40(10^{-6})$ slugs/ft-sec] flows from a supply tank through 600 ft of 2-in. diameter steel pipe ($K =$

0.0017) to discharge above a tank car, as shown in Fig. 6-13. A siphon is located at the midpoint of the pipe line. Determine (a) the discharge in gpm, and (b) the distance below the level of the kerosene in the supply tank that the siphon flows full.

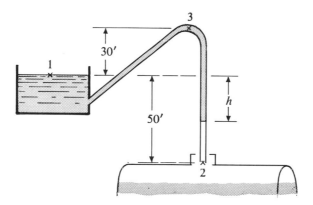

FIGURE 6-13

Solution: Following the steps outlined above, write a Bernoulli equation from point 1 to point 2, as shown in Fig. 6-13. Thus,

$$0 + 0 + 0 = 0 - 50 + \frac{v_2^2}{64.4} + \frac{0.02(600)}{\frac{1}{6}} \frac{v_2^2}{64.4}$$

from which

$$\frac{73v_2^2}{64.4} = 50.$$

Therefore,

$$v_2 = \left[\frac{50(64.4)}{73}\right]^{1/2} = \left(\frac{3220}{73}\right)^{1/2} = 6.63 \text{ fps.}$$

Since f was assumed, it must be checked.

$$\frac{K}{d} = \frac{0.0017}{2} = 0.00085$$

and,

$$N_r = \frac{50.6}{32.2} \frac{(6.63)}{6} \frac{10^6}{40} = 43,400,$$

for which $f = 0.024$.

Recalculating the velocity, using $f = 0.024$,

$$v = \left(\frac{3220}{87.4}\right)^{1/2} = 6.11 \text{ fps.}$$

Again checking f,

$$N_r = \frac{50.6}{32.2}\frac{6.11}{6}\frac{10^6}{40} = 40,000$$

and $f = 0.0245$, which is within 10 percent of the assumed value and, therefore, satisfactory.

Now, write the Bernoulli equation from point 1 to point 3 and solve for the pressure at point 3.

$$0 + 0 + 0 = \frac{p_3}{\gamma} + 30 + \frac{6.11^2}{64.4} + 0.0245(3600)\frac{6.11^2}{64.4},$$

from which

$$\frac{p_3}{\gamma} = -30 - 89.2\frac{6.11^2}{64.4} = -30 - 51.7 = -81.7 \text{ ft kerosene.}$$

Since this is much less than the minimum head possible, it is not valid.

Now, follow step 5 and write the Bernoulli equation to point 3, using the minimum allowable pressure head at the summit.

The minimum pressure head plus vapor pressure head allowed is

$$\frac{-14.7(144)}{50.6} + 0.40 = -41.8 + 0.40 = -41.4 \text{ ft of kerosene.}$$

Thus,

$$0 + 0 + 0 = -41.4 + 30 + \frac{v_3^2}{64.4} + 0.0245(3600)\frac{v_3^2}{64.4}$$

and

$$v_3 = \left[\frac{64.4(11.4)}{89.2}\right]^{1/2} = \left(\frac{734}{89.2}\right)^{1/2} = 2.87 \text{ fps.}$$

Since the velocity is considerably less at point 3 than at point 2, the value of f must again be checked.

$$N_r = 1.57\frac{(2.87)}{6}\frac{10^6}{40} = 18,750,$$

for which $f = 0.028$.

Recalculating the velocity, using $f = 0.028$,

$$v_3 = \left[\frac{64.4(11.4)}{101.8}\right]^{1/2} = 2.69 \text{ fps.}$$

Again,

$$N_r = 1.57 \frac{(2.69)}{6} \frac{10^6}{40} = 17,600,$$

for which $f = 0.028$.

Therefore,

$$Q = 2.69 \frac{(3.14)}{144} = 0.0587 \text{ cfs,}$$

or

$$Q = 0.0587(60)7.48 = 26.4 \text{ gpm.}$$

(b) To determine the distance below the level of kerosene in the supply tank that the siphon flows full, write a Bernoulli equation to some point, h distant below the surface of the supply tank. Assume the pipe runs full. Thus,

$$0 + 0 + 0 = 0 + -h + \frac{2.69^2}{64.4} + 0.028 \frac{(550 + h)}{\frac{1}{6}} \frac{2.69^2}{64.4},$$

and

$$h = 0.112 + 0.112(92.4) + 0.112h(0.168)$$

so

$$h = 0.019h + 10.46$$

and

$$0.981h = 10.46.$$

Therefore,

$$h = 10.7 \text{ ft,}$$

that is, the pipe will flow full 10.7 ft below the surface of the kerosene in the supply tank.

PROBLEMS

6-49. Water at 32°F is to be siphoned from one tank to another. Determine the maximum height to which the siphon may rise in the pipe if the tanks are located 10,000 ft above sea level.

6-50. To what maximum height may mercury at 68°F be siphoned at sea level?

6-51. Water is discharged from a reservoir through a 4-in.-diameter siphon that rises to a height of 22 ft above the water level in the reservoir. The friction head loss between the reservoir and the summit of the siphon is 6 ft of water and the loss between the summit and the discharge end is 10 ft of water. If the tank is at an elevation of 1000 ft above sea level, how far below the water level in the reservoir will the siphon flow full without causing cavitation?

6-52. A 6-in. cast iron pipe, 1200 ft long, carries kerosene "A" at 60°F from an open supply tank to a receiving tank. The discharge end of the pipe is submerged. The liquid surface in the receiving tank is 100 feet below the liquid level in the supply tank. Determine the maximum height to which the midpoint of the 1200 ft line may be elevated above the surface of the supply tank without completely stopping flow.

6-53. Water at 32°F is siphoned from a tank through a 2-in. steel pipe, 600 ft long, to discharge into the air at a point 15 ft below the water level in the tank. From the tank to the summit, which is 10 ft above the water level in the tank, there is 200 ft of pipe. Determine the discharge.

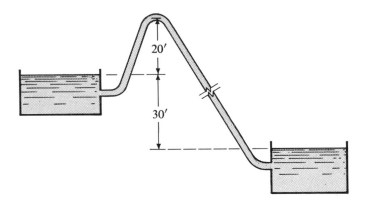

FIGURE P 6-54

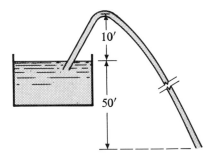

FIGURE P 6-55

6-54. Water at approximately 32°F is siphoned from a tank through 300 ft of 3-in. steel pipe and discharges into a tank, as shown in Fig. P 6-54. The length of pipe between the inlet and summit is 30 ft. Determine the probable discharge. Assume the siphon is operating at sea level.

6-55. Water at 32°F is siphoned from a tank through 200 ft of 1-in. wrought iron pipe and discharges into the air, as shown in Fig. P 6-55. If the length of pipe between the summit and the discharge end of the pipe is 150 ft, determine the probable discharge. Assume that the siphon is operating at sea level.

Chapter 7

Orifices and Short Tubes

7-1 INTRODUCTION

The flow through an orifice or short tube is similar to the flow that occurs in a venturi meter or orifice meter. In the case of the venturi meter and orifice meter, an experimentally derived coefficient was used to take care of the friction loss due to the reduced section. In the case of the orifice and short tube, similar coefficients need to be found. Again, the Bernoulli equation is used as a basis for the analysis. The general procedure is to determine the ideal velocity, assuming no friction, and then determine a coefficient of velocity that will give the actual velocity.

7-2 THE ORIFICE

Figure 7-1 shows a sharp-edged orifice discharging a liquid from a large tank into the air. As the liquid passes through the orifice the streamlines converge until the area of the stream becomes a minimum at the section called the *vena contracta*. Since the area of the jet becomes smaller between the orifice and the vena contracta, the velocity increases and the pressure decreases until it becomes atmospheric, or zero gage, at the vena contracta.

If the orifice has rounded edges the area of the stream at the vena contracta may be as large as the area of the orifice producing a greater discharge than the discharge through a sharp-edged orifice. The coefficients of velocity and contraction will vary with the shape of the edge of the orifice. The sharp-edged orifice is called the standard orifice. For this type of orifice, the coefficients remain approximately constant.

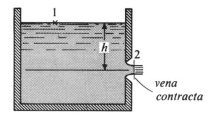

FIGURE 7-1

In order to develop an expression for the velocity of the fluid at the vena contracta, the Bernoulli equation is written from a point on the surface of the fluid in the tank to the vena contracta where the gage pressure is zero (with the exception of the pressure due to surface tension, which is negligible). Thus, taking the reference plane through the center of the orifice of Fig. 7-1, the Bernoulli equation becomes

$$0 + h + 0 = 0 + 0 + \frac{v_2^2}{2g} + h_f.$$

Neglecting the friction loss, h_f, this expression reduces to

$$v_{2(\text{ideal})} = (2gh)^{1/2}.$$

This formula is the same as that given for a freely falling body starting from rest, and is known as the *Torricelli formula*.

Introducing a coefficient of velocity, which is determined experimentally, to provide for the friction loss, this expression becomes

$$v_{2(\text{act'l})} = C_v(2gh)^{1/2}. \qquad (7\text{-}1)$$

This equation gives the actual velocity at the vena contracta (point 2).

In order to determine the discharge, the area of the vena contracta, a_2, is needed. Since the coefficient of contraction, C_c, equals a_2/a_o, the area a_2 may be expressed in terms of the area of the orifice. That is

$$a_2 = C_c a_o$$

where a_o is the area of the orifice. Thus, the expression for discharge becomes

$$Q = a_2v_2 = C_c a_o C_v (2gh)^{1/2} = C_d a_o (2gh)^{1/2} \qquad (7\text{-}2)$$

where C_d, the coefficient of discharge, is the product of C_v and C_c.

A standard orifice is a sharp-edged orifice. The coefficients, C_v and C_c, for a sharp-edged, or standard, orifice increase somewhat as the diameter of the orifice and the head increase. However, average values, which will be used in this text, are:

$$C_v = 0.98$$
$$C_c = 0.61$$
$$C_d = 0.60$$

Example 7-1. Determine the discharge in cfs through a standard 2-in.-diameter orifice located 9 ft below the water surface of a tank, as shown in Fig. 7-2.

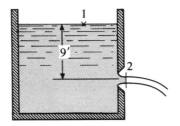

FIGURE 7-2

Solution: The coefficient of discharge for a standard orifice is 0.60. Using Eq. (7-2),

$$Q = 0.60 \frac{(3.14)}{144} [2(32.2)9]^{1/2} = 0.315 \text{ cfs.}$$

Example 7-2. A closed tank, as shown in Fig. 7-3, is divided by a partition containing a 1-in.-diameter standard orifice. Water stands to a depth of 16 ft above the orifice and the gage pressure above the water surface is 10 psi. On the discharge side of the partition the water level is below the orifice and a vacuum gage indicates 8 inches of mercury. Determine the discharge.

Solution: The difference in pressure head between the left and right of the partition of the tank can be expressed as

$$h = 16 + \frac{10}{0.433} - \frac{-8}{12} (13.6) = 48.2 \text{ ft of water.}$$

Therefore, the discharge can be expressed by Eq. (7-2) as

$$Q = 0.60 \frac{(3.14)}{576} [64.4(48.2)]^{1/2} = 0.182 \text{ cfs.}$$

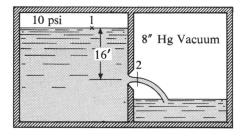

FIGURE 7-3

7-3 HEAD LOSS IN ORIFICE

The head loss in an orifice may be determined by substituting the value of the actual velocity, from Eq. (7-1), into the Bernoulli equation, which includes the head loss, h_f. Thus, referring to Fig. 7-1, the Bernoulli equation is,

$$0 + h + 0 = 0 + 0 + \frac{v_2^2}{2g} + h_f,$$

in which v_2 is the actual velocity indicated in Eq. (7-1).

Solving for h in Eq. (7-1) gives,

$$h = \frac{1}{C_v^2} \frac{v_2^2}{2g}.$$

Substituting this value of h into the Bernoulli equation gives

$$\frac{1}{C_v^2} \frac{v_2^2}{2g} = \frac{v_2^2}{2g} + h_f.$$

Therefore,

$$h_f = \left(\frac{1}{C_v^2} - 1\right) \frac{v_2^2}{2g},$$

which is the head loss in an orifice discharging from a tank in which the initial velocity is zero or is so small that it may be neglected.

7-4 THE SHORT TUBE

A short tube is one that has a length about two and one-half times greater than the diameter. If the entrance to the tube is sharp-cornered, it is called a standard short tube, as shown in Fig. 7-4(a).

The equation for fluid flow through a short tube is similar to the equation for an orifice and is developed by using the basic Bernoulli equation. Since the tube flows full, point 2 is taken at the end of the tube, where the area of the stream is the same as the area of the tube and the pressure is zero. The equation for the velocity in a short tube is

$$v_2 = C_v (2gh)^{1/2} \qquad (7\text{-}3)$$

and the equation of discharge is

$$Q = C_v C_c a_o (2gh)^{1/2} = C_d a_o (2gh)^{1/2}. \qquad (7\text{-}4)$$

For the standard (sharp-cornered) short tube, average values for the coefficients are

$$C_v = 0.82$$
$$C_c = 1.00$$
$$C_d = 0.82$$

The equation for the head loss in an orifice applies, also, to the head loss in a short tube.

A condition may exist where the head on the short tube is so large that the tube will not run full but will operate as an orifice, as shown in Fig. 7-4(b). Since a vacuum is produced at section A–A of Fig. 7-4(a), the liquid will spring free of the tube when the vacuum approaches the absolute zero pressure minus the vapor pressure. The head to produce this vacuum is approximately 38 feet of water at sea level. This head may be determined by writing the Bernoulli equations from point 1 to section A–A, and from point 1 to the end of the tube, letting the pressure at section A–A approach absolute zero. Thus, writing the Bernoulli equation from point 1 to section A–A, gives,

$$0 + h + 0 = -33.7 + 0 + \frac{v_A^2}{2g} + \left(\frac{1}{C_v^2} - 1\right)\frac{v_A^2}{2g}$$

$$33.7 + h + 0 = \frac{1}{C_v^2}\frac{v_A^2}{2g}$$

where 33.7 is the atmospheric pressure head at sea level minus the vapor pressure. C_v, in this case, would be the same as for an orifice, or 0.98, therefore

$$\frac{v_A^2}{2g} = (33.7 + h)0.96. \qquad (7\text{-}5)$$

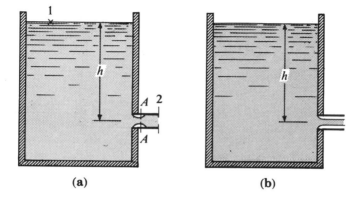

FIGURE 7-4

The Bernoulli equation from point 1 to the end of the tube, point 2, gives,

$$0 + h + 0 = 0 + 0 + \frac{v_2^2}{2g} + \left(\frac{1}{C_v^2} - 1\right)\frac{v_2^2}{2g}$$

and

$$h = \frac{1}{C_v^2}\frac{v_2^2}{2g}.$$

Since C_v for a standard short tube is 0.82,

$$\frac{v_2^2}{2g} = 0.672h. \qquad (7\text{-}6)$$

Since the area of the vena contracta is 0.61 times the area of the tube,

$$\frac{v_2}{v_A} = \frac{0.61d^2}{d^2} \qquad \text{or} \qquad v_2 = 0.61v_A.$$

Therefore,

$$\frac{v_2^2}{2g} = 0.372\frac{v_A^2}{2g},$$

and from Eq. (7-6),

$$\frac{v_A^2}{2g} = \frac{0.672}{0.372} h. \tag{7-7}$$

The velocity heads in Eq. (7-5) and Eq. (7-7) are the same, therefore,

$$\frac{0.672}{0.372} h = (33.7 + h)0.96.$$

Solving for h,

$$1.81h = 32.35 + 0.96h$$

and

$$h = 38.1 \text{ ft.}$$

A greater head will cause the stream to spring free of the sides and flow as an orifice, as indicated in Fig. 7-4(b).

Example 7-3. Water flows from a closed tank through a 3-in.-diameter standard short tube, as shown in Fig. 7-5. Determine the discharge when the water surface is 12 ft above the short tube and the pressure above the water surface is 7.8 psi.

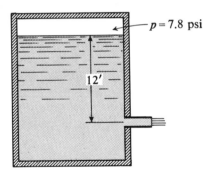

FIGURE 7-5

Solution: The total head producing flow is

$$h = 12 + \frac{7.8}{0.433} = 12 + 18 = 30 \text{ ft}$$

Since this is less than 38 ft, the short tube will flow full. Therefore, the discharge, by Eq. (7-4) is

$$Q = 0.82 \frac{(3.14)}{64} [64.4(30)]^{1/2} = 1.77 \text{ cfs.}$$

PROBLEMS

7-1.   How much water will be discharged through a standard 1-in.-diameter orifice, located 9 ft below the water surface of an open tank?

7-2.   How much water will be discharged through a standard 2-in.-diameter short tube, located 16 ft below the water surface of an open tank?

7-3.   A standard 2-in.-diameter orifice is located 16 feet below the water surface in a closed tank. If the pressure gage at the top of the tank reads 10 psi, determine the discharge.

7-4.   Determine the head loss in Prob. 7-1.

7-5.   Determine the head loss in Prob. 7-3.

7-6.   A 1-in.-diameter orifice discharges 1900 lb of water in 4 minutes under a constant head of 25 ft. The jet diameter at the vena contracta is 0.785 in. Determine the coefficient of velocity and the coefficient of contraction.

7-7.   What diameter of standard orifice will discharge 3 cfs under a head of 36 ft?

7-8.   A 1.50-in. circular orifice discharges 500 lb of water in 1.80 minutes under a head of 1.5 ft. The diameter of the vena contracta is 1.30 in. Determine the coefficient of velocity.

7-9.   A standard 3-in. square orifice, for which the coefficient of discharge is 0.60, discharges 2.50 cfs of water. Determine the head.

7-10.   A 3-in.-diameter standard orifice discharges water under a head of 36 ft. If all of the friction loss in the orifice occurs between the plane of the orifice and the vena contracta, determine the pressure in the plane of the orifice.

7-11.   How much water will be discharged from a 1-in.-diameter standard short tube under a head of 16 ft?

7-12.   A 2-in.-diameter short tube discharges water under a head of 36 ft. If the characteristics of the tube are the same as those of a standard orifice up to the vena contracta, section *A-A* in Figure. 7-4, determine the pressure at this section.

7-13.   Determine the approximate maximum head under which a standard short tube will flow full when it is discharging water at 100°F at an elevation of 3000 ft.

7-14.   Determine the head required to discharge 0.785 cfs of water through a 2-in. standard short tube.

7-15.   What diameter of standard short tube will be needed if it is to discharge 1.57 cfs. of water when flowing full under a head of 36 ft?

7-16.   A 2-in.-diameter standard orifice under a head of 25 ft is to be replaced by a standard short tube. Determine the diameter of the tube if it is to discharge the same amount of water as the orifice.

Chapter 8

Steady Flow of Liquids—
Open Channels

8-1 INTRODUCTION

In the previous chapters the flow of fluids in closed conduits under pressure was considered. Liquid is transported, also, in open channels and the flow depends primarily on the slope and shape of the channel. The discharge generally is measured by *weirs*, although other special measuring devices, such as the Parshall flume, are sometimes used.

8-2 OPEN CHANNELS

An open channel is subject only to atmospheric pressure so that the flow is produced primarily by the slope of the channel. As mentioned above, the shape of the channel also affects the amount of discharge. Although the determination of the flow or discharge in an open channel lends itself to rational analysis with the use of the Bernoulli equation, unknown factors enter into the solution, especially due to cross-currents in the stream, so that certain experimentally derived coefficients must be introduced to produce a valid formula.

Most open-channel formulas are empirically determined by assuming a channel of constant cross section in which the velocity remains unchanged. To develop such a formula, assume a portion of a channel as indicated in Fig. 8-1. Points 1 and 2 are located on any streamline. The reference plane is taken at point 2.

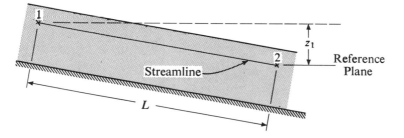

FIGURE 8-1

The Bernoulli equation, written from point 1 to point 2, gives

$$\frac{p_1}{\gamma} + z_1 + \frac{v_1^2}{2g} = \frac{p_2}{\gamma} + 0 + \frac{v_2^2}{2g} + h_f.$$

Since the velocities and the pressures are the same at points 1 and 2, this equation reduces to

$$z_1 = h_f. \tag{8-1}$$

Since this is a noncircular section, a new relationship is necessary to replace the diameter, d, in the head loss equation

$$h_f = f\frac{L}{d}\frac{v^2}{2g}.$$

This new quantity, R, known as the *hydraulic radius*, or the hydraulic mean depth, is defined as the cross-sectional area of the stream divided by the wetted perimeter. That is,

$$R = \frac{a}{p}$$

where p is the wetted perimeter.

The hydraulic radius of a closed pipe is

$$R = \frac{\pi d^2}{4\pi d} = \frac{d}{4}$$

so that $d = 4R$. Substituting this value for d into the equation for lost head gives

$$h_f = f \frac{L}{4R} \frac{v^2}{2g}. \tag{8-2}$$

Equation (8-2) gives the correct results if the proper coefficient, f, is used. The value of f, determined experimentally, will depend on the Reynolds number, the roughness of the channel, and the shape of the channel section. Substituting Eq. (8-1) into Eq. (8-2) gives

$$z_1 = f \frac{L}{4R} \frac{v^2}{2g}$$

where z_1 is the drop in elevation of the fluid in the channel in the distance L. Then,

$$\frac{z_1}{L} = \frac{fv^2}{8Rg}.$$

However, z_1/L is approximately equivalent to the slope of the channel for small values of the slope, so that

$$s = \frac{fv^2}{8Rg}$$

where s is the slope of the channel. Therefore,

$$v = \left(\frac{8g}{f}\right)^{1/2} (Rs)^{1/2}.$$

Now, let

$$C = \left(\frac{8g}{f}\right)^{1/2}.$$

Then,

$$v = C(Rs)^{1/2}. \tag{8-3}$$

Equation (8-3) is known as the *Chézy formula* for flow in an open channel. This formula requires the evaluation of the coefficient C which depends in turn on the coefficient f. By substituting the term $(1.486R^{1/6})/n$ for C, Eq. (8-3) becomes,

$$v = \frac{1.486}{n} R^{2/3} s^{1/2}, \tag{8-4}$$

which is known as the *Manning formula*. In this formula, $1.486/n$ may be replaced by K, when the roughness coefficient is given in terms of K. The coefficients K and n are dependent only on the roughness of the channel and the properties of the fluid. They are not dimensionless. Values of K and n are given in Table 7 for various materials used in the construction of channels.

TABLE 7[1]

VALUES OF n AND K FOR THE MANNING FORMULA*

Surface Material	n	K
Brick, Glazed	0.013	114
Clay tile	0.014	106
Clay, Vitrified	0.013	114
Concrete	0.015	99
Earth (good condition)	0.023	65
Earth (poor condition)	0.035	42
Metal, Smooth	0.013	114
Metal, Corrugated	0.026	57
Stone Masonry, Smooth	0.015	99
Stone Masonry, Rough	0.025	59
Stone (excavated channel)	0.033	45
Timber, Planed	0.012	124
Timber, Unplaned	0.013	114

* Values are valid only for water at ordinary temperatures.

Although other empirical open-channel formulas have been developed, the Manning formula gives good results where the cross section of the channel and the velocity of the fluid do not change.

The discharge, Q, for an open channel, using the Manning formula, is

$$Q = a \frac{1.486}{n} R^{2/3} s^{1/2} \quad \text{or} \quad aKR^{2/3}s^{1/2}. \tag{8-5}$$

Example 8-1. A semicircular concrete-lined canal, having a radius of 5 ft, is laid to a slope of 9 ft in 10,000 ft. Determine the discharge when the canal flows full.

1. Values in Table 7 were taken from the text, *Properties of Fluids*, by permission of the author, Dr. Glenn Murphy.

Solution: Figure 8-2 is a sketch of the semi-circular channel. From Table 7, the roughness coefficient, K, is 99. The hydraulic radius, R, is computed as

$$R = \frac{a}{p} = \frac{\pi 5^2}{2\pi 5} = \frac{5}{2} = 2.5 \text{ ft.}$$

Since $Q = aKR^{2/3}s^{1/2}$, therefore,

$$Q = \frac{\pi 25}{2}(99)2.5^{2/3}(0.03) = 215 \text{ cfs.}$$

FIGURE 8-2

Example 8-2. A rectangular flume, designed to carry 100 cfs of water, is to be constructed of rough stone masonry with the depth of flow equal to one-half the width of the channel. It is placed on a slope of 0.16 ft/100 ft. Determine the minimum dimensions of the flume.

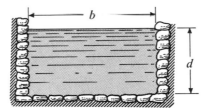

FIGURE 8-3

Solution: For rough stone masonry, the roughness coefficient, K, is 59. Refer to Fig. 8-3. Since the width b equals $2d$, the hydraulic radius, R, of this flume is computed as

$$R = \frac{2d^2}{4d} = \frac{d}{2}.$$

Therefore, since $Q = aKR^{2/3}s^{1/2}$,

$$100 = 2d^2 59 \left(\frac{d}{2}\right)^{2/3} 0.04$$

and,

$$d = \left[\frac{(100)1.59(100)}{2(59)4}\right]^{3/8} = 33.7^{3/8} = 3.74 \text{ ft}$$

and,

$$b = 2(3.74) = 7.48 \text{ ft.}$$

Example 8-3.   A drainage ditch, built in earth in good condition ($n = 0.023$), has a base width of 10 ft and side slopes of one vertical to two horizontal. Determine the slope necessary to produce a discharge of 400 cfs when the ditch flows to a depth of 4 ft.

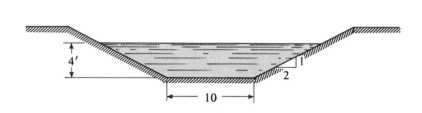

FIGURE 8-4

Solution: Refer to Fig. 8-4. The area of flow is $32 + 40 = 72$ sq ft and the wetted perimeter is $10 + 2(80)^{1/2} = 10 + 2(8.94) = 27.88$ ft. Therefore,

$$R = \frac{72}{27.88} = 2.58.$$

Since $Q = (a1.486R^{2/3}s^{1/2})/n$,

$$s^{1/2} = \frac{400}{[(72)1.486(2.58)^{2/3}]/0.023} = 0.0454.$$

Therefore,

$$s = 0.0454^2 = 0.00206 \text{ (slope).}$$

PROBLEMS

8-1.   If the hydraulic radius is equal to one-half the depth of flow, determine the ratio of width to depth of a rectangular channel.

8-2.   A channel with a trapezoidal cross-section has a base width of 16 ft and side slopes of 1 vertical to 2 horizontal. Determine the hydraulic radius when the depth of water in the channel is 8 ft.

8-3. Determine the discharge through the channel of Prob. 8-2, if it is laid on a grade of 0.40 ft/1000 ft in earth in good condition.

8-4. A rectangular channel, 12 ft wide, is lined with smooth stone masonry and is laid on a slope of 8.1 ft/1000 ft. Determine the discharge when the depth of water is 5 ft.

8-5. Determine the slope on which the channel in Prob. 8-2 must be laid if it is to carry 240 cfs through a channel lined with corrugated metal.

8-6. On what slope should a rectangular flume of planed timber be laid if it is to carry 180 cfs when the depth of water is 4 ft and the width of the channel is 10 ft?

8-7. Determine the minimum slope required for a semicircular flume, 8 ft in diameter and flowing full, to discharge 120 cfs ($K = 99$).

8-8. A semicircular concrete-lined channel flowing full discharges into a rectangular planed-timber flume 5 ft wide. Both channels are laid on a grade of 3 ft/mile. Determine the minimum diameter of the concrete channel if the maximum depth of water in the timber flume is to be 4 ft.

8-9. Water flows at a depth of 2.5 ft in a rectangular channel 6 ft wide and excavated from stone on a slope of 1 ft/100 ft. Determine the diameter of a semicircular concrete flume, flowing full, which will have the same capacity when laid on the same slope.

8-10. A concrete canal, having side slopes of 2 vertical to 1 horizontal and laid on a grade of 3.6 ft/1000 ft, is to carry the discharge from two smooth stone masonry flumes each 8 ft wide and 4 ft deep, and both laid on a 1 percent slope. If the base width of the concrete canal is to be twice the depth of water, determine its dimensions.

8-11. A 3-ft-diameter corrugated metal culvert, flowing half full, is to carry the discharge from a channel 3 ft wide by 2 ft deep, with side slopes of 1 vertical to 3 horizontal on a grade of 1.6 ft/1000 ft, built in earth in good condition. Determine the required slope of the metal culvert.

8-12. A semicircular concrete-lined canal 6 ft in diameter, flowing full and carrying 240 cfs, discharges into a rectangular concrete-lined canal 6 ft wide. If the two canals have the same slope, determine the depth of the water in the rectangular canal.

8-13. A discharge of 114 cfs of water is flowing through a rectangular channel, 6 ft wide, at a depth of 4 ft. The slope of the channel is 0.0009. Determine the channel coefficient, K.

8-14. An 8-ft-diameter circular concrete flume, flowing half full, is laid on a 1 percent slope. Determine the probable discharge.

8-15. A rectangular channel has a width of 10 ft. When the water is 3 ft deep in the channel the discharge is 50 cfs. Determine the discharge when the depth is 5 ft.

8-16. A rectangular flume of planed timber is 10 ft wide and is to discharge 200 cfs of water when the depth is 5 ft. Determine the slope on which the flume should be laid.

8-17. A rectangular concrete flume is 6 ft wide and laid on a slope of 2.5 ft/1000 ft. Determine the discharge when the water flows at a depth of 3 ft. ($K = 100$.)

8-18. A rectangular open channel ($n = 0.01486$) is to be built to carry a minimum discharge of 200 cfs with a maximum velocity of 10 fps. Determine the least required dimensions of the channel if it is laid on a slope of 1 percent. $K = 100$.

8-19. A concrete channel ($n = 0.015$) has a trapezoidal cross section with a base width of 4 ft and side slopes of 3 vertical to 4 horizontal. When the depth of flow is 3 ft, determine the necessary slope to produce a discharge of 400 cfs.

8-3 MOST EFFICIENT CROSS SECTIONS

The shape or dimensions of the cross section of an open channel determines the efficiency of the channel; that is, the greatest discharge for a given area, slope, and roughness, will have the least wetted perimeter. The Manning formula indicates that for a given slope, s, and coefficient, K, or n, the discharge is dependent on the hydraulic radius, a/p. Thus, for a constant area, the discharge is maximum when the wetted perimeter is a minimum.

Of all possible shapes, the semicircular channel has the smallest perimeter for a given area and, therefore, is the most efficient of all shapes. However, semicircular channels are not as easily constructed as other types of channels. A rectangular, trapezoidal, or V-notch shape is often used. For each particular shape used there is a ratio of base width to depth of stream, or angle of the notch, that gives the most efficient cross section.

Note: The following discussion involves calculus.

This ratio may be determined by setting up an expression for the wetted perimeter in terms of the ratio of base width to depth and differentiating to find the minimum perimeter in terms of this ratio. For example, assume a trapezoidal cross section of a channel, as shown in Fig. 8-5, for which the dimensions of the most efficient section is to be determined.

The wetted perimeter, which is to be a minimum, is

$$p = b + 2d(1^2 + 1^2)^{1/2} = b + 2.828d.$$

Also, the area is

$$a = bd + d^2$$

Since there are two variables, b and d, the equation must be simplified in order to differentiate. Let $q = b/d$. Then $b = qd$, and

$$a = qd^2 + d^2 = d^2(q + 1).$$

Therefore,

$$d = \left(\frac{a}{q+1}\right)^{1/2}$$

Also, substituting qd for b in the equation for the wetted perimeter gives

$$p = qd + 2.828d = d(q + 2.828).$$

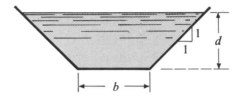

FIGURE 8-5

Substituting the value of d into this equation results in

$$p = \left(\frac{a}{q+1}\right)^{1/2}(q + 2.828).$$

By differentiating the perimeter, p, with respect to q, and equating to zero, the minimum value of the perimeter may be found. Thus,

$$\frac{dp}{dq} = (q + 1)^{1/2} - \frac{1}{2}\frac{(q + 2.828)}{(q + 1)^{1/2}} = 0.$$

Multiplying by $(q + 1)^{1/2}$ results in

$$q + 1 = \frac{1}{2}(q + 2.828) = \frac{q}{2} + 1.414$$

and

$$q = 0.828.$$

Therefore, $b/d = 0.828$, and

$$b = 0.828d$$

for the most efficient section.

Since $R = a/p$, then

$$R = \frac{bd + d^2}{b + 2d(2)^{1/2}} = \frac{0.828d^2 + d^2}{0.828d + 2.828d} = \frac{d}{2}. \tag{8-6}$$

It is found that for the most efficient trapezoidal, and rectangular sections, the hydraulic radius, R, is always equal to $d/2$, where d is the depth of the channel. This fact simplifies the determination of the ratio of b/d since the ratio can be determined by equating the hydraulic radius in terms of b and d to the value $d/2$. For example, refer to the Fig. 8-5:

$$R = \frac{a}{p} = \frac{bd + d^2}{b + 2d(2)^{1/2}} = \frac{d}{2}.$$

Then,

$$2bd + 2d^2 = bd + 2.828d^2$$

and

$$bd = 0.828d^2 \quad \text{or} \quad b = 0.828d,$$

which is the same as the value determined by using calculus.

The most efficient V-shaped open channel is one that has an angle, θ, of 45° at the apex, as shown in Fig. 8-6, or a total apex angle of 90°.

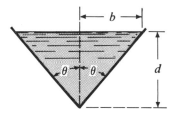

FIGURE 8-6

Note: The following discussion involves calculus.

The value of θ, in Fig. 8-6, for the most efficient V-shaped section may be determined by differentiating the wetted perimeter, p, with respect to ratio b/d, as was done for the trapezoidal shapes. By letting $q = b/d$, $b = qd$. Also

$$a = bd = qd^2$$

and

$$d = \left(\frac{a}{q}\right)^{1/2}.$$

Also,

$$p = 2(b^2 + d^2)^{1/2} = 2(q^2d^2 + d^2)^{1/2} = 2d(q^2 + 1)^{1/2}.$$

Differentiating p with respect to q, and equating to zero results in

$$\frac{dp}{dq} = q^{1/2}\frac{1}{2}(q^2 + 1)^{-1/2}2q - (q^2 + 1)^{1/2}\frac{1}{2}q^{-1/2} = 0.$$

Therefore,

$$\frac{q^{3/2}}{q(q^2 + 1)} = \frac{(q^2 + 1)^{1/2}}{q^{3/2}}$$

and

$$q^2 = 1, \qquad q = 1, \qquad \text{and} \qquad b/d = 1.$$

Therefore, $\theta = 45°$, and the apex angle $= 90°$ for the most efficient V-shaped section.

Example 8-4.   An earth channel with side slopes of 1 vertical to 3 horizontal is to discharge 100 cfs. Determine the most efficient section if the slope of the channel is 1.6 ft/1000 ft of length. ($K = 65$.)

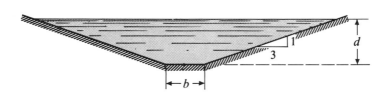

FIGURE 8-7

Solution: Figure 8-7 is the cross section of the channel. Since $R = d/2$ for the most efficient section for this shape,

$$\frac{d}{2} = \frac{a}{p} = \frac{bd + 3d^2}{b + 2d(10^{1/2})}$$

and

$$bd + 2d^2(10^{1/2}) = 2bd + 6d^2.$$

Therefore,

$$b = 3.162(2d) - 6d = 0.324d.$$

The expanded Manning formula for discharge is $Q = aKR^{2/3}s^{1/2}$. Substituting known values into this equation results in the equation,

$$100 = (0.324d^2 + 3d^2)65 \left(\frac{d}{2}\right)^{2/3} 0.04$$

and

$$100 = 3.324d^2(65) \frac{d^{2/3}}{1.59} (0.04).$$

Therefore,

$$d^{8/3} = \frac{159}{8.64} = 18.4$$

and

$$d - 2.98 \text{ ft.}$$

Since $b = 0.324d$,

$$b = 0.324(2.98) = 0.966 \text{ ft.}$$

Example 8-5. A semicircular concrete flume, Fig. 8-8, flows full at a slope of 2.5 ft/1000 ft and is to discharge 150 cfs. Determine the dimensions of the flume. The friction coefficient, n, is 0.015.

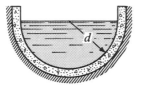

FIGURE 8-8

Solution: Since $R = d/2$, the expression for the discharge, using the Manning formula, is

$$Q = a \frac{1.486}{n} \left(\frac{d}{2}\right)^{2/3} s^{1/2}.$$

Then,

$$150 = \frac{3.14d^2}{2} \left(\frac{1.486}{0.015}\right) \frac{d^{2/3}}{1.59} 0.05$$

and

$$d^{8/3} = \frac{716}{23.2} = 30.7.$$

Therefore,

$$d = 3.61 \text{ ft},$$

which is the radius of the semicircular channel.

Example 8-6. A most efficient triangular open channel, Fig. 8-9, made of planed timber, flows at a maximum depth of 3 ft on a grade of 16 ft/mile. Determine the discharge.

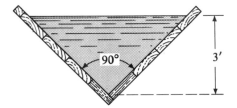

FIGURE 8-9

Solution: From Fig. 8-9, the area of the stream is 9 sq ft. Using the Manning formula,

$$Q = 9(124) \left[\frac{9}{2(18^{1/2})} \right]^{2/3} \left(\frac{16}{5280} \right)^{1/2}.$$

Therefore,

$$Q = 1116(1.064)^{2/3} \frac{4}{72.67} = 63.9 \text{ cfs}.$$

PROBLEMS

8-20. A channel ($K = 65$) has a trapezoidal cross section with a base width of 10 ft and side slopes of 1 to 1. The channel is laid to a 0.09 percent grade. Determine the discharge when at a depth that gives a cross section of maximum efficiency.

8-21. A trapezoidal flume ($K = 124$) with side slopes of 3 horizontal to 4 vertical discharges into a circular channel ($K = 106$). If the circular channel is to be 5 ft in diameter and is to have a slope equal to one-half the slope of the trapezoidal flume, determine the dimensions of the trapezoidal flume so it will have its most efficient cross section when the circular channel is flowing half full.

8-22. Determine the dimensions of the most efficient trapezoidal cross section having side slopes of 4 vertical to 3 horizontal, which could replace the symmetrical V-shaped channel of Fig. P 8-22. The trapezoidal channel is to be lined with the same material and laid on the same slope as the V-shaped channel.

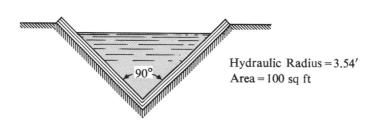

Hydraulic Radius = 3.54′
Area = 100 sq ft

FIGURE P 8-22

8-23. A stone channel ($n = 0.033$) has a trapezoidal cross section with a base width of 12 ft and side slopes of 1 to 1. The channel is laid on a slope of 9 ft/mile. Determine the discharge when at a depth that gives a cross section of maximum efficiency.

8-24. Determine the diameter of a circular culvert ($K = 114$) that, when flowing half full, will carry the discharge from an open rectangular channel ($n = 0.033$) having a base width of 6 feet and flowing at a depth that gives a cross section of maximum efficiency. The culvert is to be laid on a slope 4 times the slope of the channel.

8-25. Determine the dimensions of the most efficient rectangular flume that will carry the discharge from a 2-ft diameter circular conduit flowing half full. Both flumes are of planed timber and are on the same grade.

8-26. Determine the dimensions of the most efficient trapezoidal cross section having side slopes of 2 vertical to 3 horizontal that could replace a semicircular channel having a radius and depth of flow of 4 ft. The trapezoidal channel is to be lined with the same material and have one-half the slope of the semicircular channel.

8-27. A stone channel ($K = 45$) has a trapezoidal cross section with a base width of 10 ft and side slopes of 1 to 1. The channel is laid on a slope of 1.6 ft/1000 ft. Determine the discharge when at a depth that gives a cross section of maximum efficiency.

8-28. A rectangular earth channel ($K = 60$) has a base width of 10 ft and is laid on a grade of 0.04 percent. It discharges into a semicircular concrete flume ($K = 100$) which has a diameter of 10 ft. Determine the required minimum slope for the flume if the rectangular channel is operating under the most efficient conditions.

8-29. A concrete channel ($K = 100$) has a trapezoidal cross section with a base width of 2 ft and side slopes of 1 vertical to 3 horizontal. When at a depth that gives a cross section of maximum efficiency, the discharge is to be 500 cfs. Determine the necessary slope.

8-30. Determine the dimensions of the most efficient trapezoidal section having side slopes of 2 vertical to 5 horizontal that could replace a rectangular channel, 8 ft wide by 3 ft deep. The trapezoidal channel is to be lined with the same material and have one-third the slope of the rectangular channel.

8-31. Determine the dimensions of the most efficient trapezoidal section of a concrete channel having side slopes of 5 vertical to 12 horizontal. The channel has a slope of 2.50 ft/1000 ft and a discharge of 500 cfs. ($K = 100$.)

8-32. Determine the necessary depth of a concrete open channel ($K = 99$) having side slopes of 1 vertical to 3 horizontal, if it is to operate under the most efficient conditions when the water flows at the rate of 100 cfs. The slope of the channel is 1.6 ft/1000 ft of length.

8-4   NONUNIFORM FLOW IN OPEN CHANNELS

It becomes necessary at times to determine the velocity, slope, and depth of a channel that will have a maximum discharge. The situation may occur at the inlet of a channel discharging from a reservoir or at a transition section, as where one channel discharges into one of different cross section, elevation, or slope. Some of the useful concepts required in such an analysis are specific energy, critical depth, and critical slope.

8-5   SPECIFIC ENERGY AND CRITICAL DEPTH

The specific energy of a fluid flowing in an open channel is the total head taken with reference to the reference plane at the bottom of the channel and at a specific cross section. If v is the average velocity of the fluid and y is the depth of the channel, then

$$E = \frac{v^2}{2g} + y \qquad (8\text{-}7)$$

where E is the specific energy. In terms of the flow rate, under steady flow,

$$E = \frac{1}{2g}\left(\frac{Q}{a}\right)^2 + y. \qquad (8\text{-}8)$$

Equations (8-7) and (8-8) assume that the pressure head at the bottom of the channel is equal to the static pressure head.

In order to simplify further computations, it is desirable to assume a wide rectangular channel. Then the specific energy will be the same for each unit width of the channel. Since the discharge equals the product of the average velocity and the cross-sectional area, the discharge for an area of unit width becomes,

$$q = y(1)v.$$

Therefore,

$$v = q/y.$$

Substituting into Eq. (8-7) gives

$$E = \frac{q^2}{2gy^2} + y \qquad (8\text{-}9)$$

and

$$q = [2g(y^2E - y^3)]^{1/2} \qquad (8\text{-}10)$$

From Eq. (8-9) it appears that for a given discharge, q, the specific energy depends on the depth, y, of the channel. If the depth is small, the energy is primarily kinetic; and, if the depth is large, the potential energy is dominant.

Note: The following discussion involves calculus.

The depth of the channel for which the specific energy is a minimum for a constant value of discharge can be determined by differentiating E with respect to y in Eq. (8-9) and equating the result to zero. Thus,

$$\frac{d}{dy}\left(\frac{q^2}{2gy_c^2} + y\right) = -\frac{2q^2 y_c^{-3}}{2g} + 1 = 0.$$

Then,

$$\frac{2q^2}{2gy_c^3} = 1$$

The depth for which the specific energy is a minimum is

$$y_c = \left(\frac{q^2}{g}\right)^{1/3}, \qquad (8\text{-}11)$$

Thus, y_c is the critical depth for which the specific energy is a minimum. Also,

$$q = v_c y_c$$

in which v_c is the critical velocity corresponding to the critical depth. Substituting this value of q into Eq. (8-11) gives

$$y_c = \left(\frac{v_c^2 y_c^2}{g}\right)^{1/3} \tag{8-12}$$

from which

$$\frac{v_c^2}{2g} = \frac{y_c}{2}.$$

Thus, when the flow is at the critical depth, the velocity head equals one-half the critical depth, that is, the kinetic energy is one-half of the potential energy.

Substituting this value of the kinetic energy into Eq. (8-7) gives

$$E = \frac{y_c}{2} + y_c = \frac{3}{2}y_c, \tag{8-13}$$

and

$$y_c = \frac{2}{3}E_{min}, \tag{8-14}$$

y	0:00	0.25	0.50	0.75	1.00	1.25	1.35	1.50
q	0.00	2.24	4.01	5.22	5.67	5.02	4.21	0.00

y	0:00	0.25	0.50	0.75	1.00	1.25	1.50	1.75	2.00
E	0.00	8.25	2.50	1.64	1.50	1.65	1.72	1.91	2.13

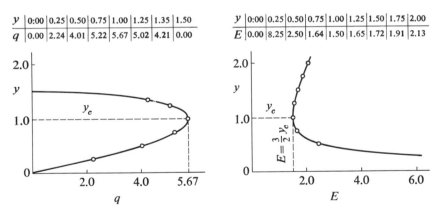

FIGURES 8-10 and 8-11

Equation (8-10) gives a relationship between specific energy, depth, and discharge. If the discharge is held constant, a depth-specific energy curve can be plotted, as shown in Fig. 8-10. Also, if the specific energy is held constant, a depth-discharge curve can be plotted, as shown in Fig. 8-11. Since these curves result from plots of the same equation, the points of minimum E and maximum q are equivalent. The depth associated with the minimum specific energy and the maximum discharge, known as the *critical depth*, is the boundary between zones of open-channel flow that have different physical character. *The flow at depths greater than the critical depth are known as subcritical, tranquil, or streaming flow; and flow at depths less than the critical depth are known as supercritical, or shooting flow.*

Where the depth is less than the critical depth, the discharge is less than maximum, but the velocity is higher than the critical velocity and this results in shooting flow. When the depth is more than the critical depth, the discharge is again less than the maximum, but the velocity is lower than the critical velocity and the flow appears tranquil, or streaming. For any specific discharge less than the maximum, there are two depths at which the specific energy is the same: one produces shooting flow and the other produces tranquil flow. The type of flow depends on the velocity and, in turn, the velocity depends on the slope of the channel.

8-6 CRITICAL SLOPE

When the slope of a channel is such as to develop the critical velocity, the slope is called the critical slope. For a given critical velocity, or critical depth, the critical slope may be found by use of the Manning formula. However, for a very wide rectangular channel, an expression for the critical slope, S_c, can be determined as follows: The Chézy equation is

$$v = C(Rs)^{1/2}.$$

In terms of the flow rate, this equation becomes

$$Q = Ca(Rs)^{1/2}. \qquad (8\text{-}15)$$

By equating the flow rates of Eq. (8-11) and (8-15),

$$q = (gy_c^3)^{1/2} = Cy_c(y_cS_c)^{1/2}.$$

Therefore,

$$S_c = \frac{g}{C^2}. \qquad (8\text{-}16)$$

However,

$$C = \frac{1.49y^{1/6}}{n}.$$

Substituting into Eq. (8-16), gives

$$S_c = \frac{gn^2}{2.2y^{1/3}},$$

which indicates that the critical slope is a function of the depth. For valid results, the value of S_c may be computed only for $y = y_c$.

PROBLEMS

8-33. Calculate the specific energies for 180 cfs flow in a rectangular channel, 12 ft wide, when the depth is (a) 1.5 ft, (b) 2.0 ft, (c) 3.0 ft, and (d) 6 ft. Also plot a depth-energy curve.

8-34. At what depths may 24 cfs flow in a rectangular channel 8 ft wide, if the specific energy is 3 ft?

8-35. Calculate the specific energies for a 240 cfs flow in a rectangular channel 20 ft wide, when the depth is (a) 1.5 ft, (b) 4 ft, and (c) 8 ft.

8-36. At what depths may 12 cfs flow in a rectangular channel 6 ft wide, if the specific energy is 2 ft?

8-37. Flow occurs in a rectangular channel that is 18 ft wide and has a specific energy of 9 ft. Plot the y-q curve. Determine from the curve (a) the maximum flow rate, (b) the critical depth, and (c) the flow rate and flow condition at depths of 3 ft and 8 ft.

8-38. If 300 cfs flows in a rectangular channel 12 ft wide, at a depth of 3 ft, is the flow subcritical or supercritical?

8-39. If 400 cfs flows in a rectangular channel 20 ft wide, with a velocity of 10 fps, is the flow shooting or tranquil?

8-40. If 360 cfs flows uniformly in a rectangular channel 15 ft wide, and laid on a slope of 0.0049 for which n equals 0.013, is the flow subcritical or supercritical? What is the critical slope for this flow rate, assuming the channel to be very wide?

8-41. The uniform flow in a rectangular channel 10 ft wide, has a specific energy of 8 ft, and the slope of the channel is 0.0044. The Chézy coefficient, C, is 120 ft$^{1/2}$/sec. Determine the depth, velocity, and flow rate of the channel.

8-42. Determine the maximum flow rate that may occur in a rectangular channel 10 ft wide, for a specific energy of 6 ft.

Chapter 9

Flow Measuring Devices
in Open Channels

9-1 STREAM GAGING

Where the sides and bottom of a stream are irregular, the use of the open-channel formulas would not be accurate. For such situations the discharge is usually determined by the method of stream gaging, using a current meter.

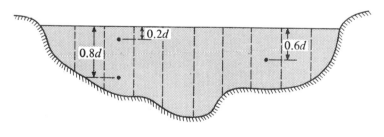

FIGURE 9-1

First, the stream is divided into sections, as shown in Fig. 9-1. The average velocity of the stream in each section is determined by placing the current meter at 0.2 and 0.8 of the depth of the stream and averaging the

177

velocities to determine the average for that section. For very accurate work section readings are taken at regular increments of depth, usually at each one-tenth increment. Rough approximations of the average velocities may be obtained by placing the current meter at 0.6 of the depth for each section.

9-2   WEIRS

Weirs are used to measure the discharge of small open channels such as irrigation ditches, drainage canals, aqueducts, or sewer plant outlets. The weir plate extends completely across the stream and extends above the surface a portion of the way so that the flow is restricted to the weir notch. The shape of the notch is, generally, rectangular, triangular, or trapezoidal, although other special shapes are sometimes used. Figure 9-2

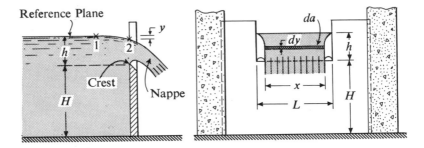

FIGURE 9-2

shows a rectangular weir. *The length of the weir, L, is the length of the crest (bottom of the notch).* The crest and sides of the notch may be sharp-edged or rounded. Since the sharp-crested weir is more easily duplicated, it is more generally used. The sides of the weir produce end contractions and, thereby, reduce the width of the nappe. *Where the weir notch extends the full width of the channel, there are no end contractions and the weir is known as a suppressed weir.*

The height of the weir, H, is the distance from the stream bed to the crest of the weir, as shown in Fig. 9-2. The nappe of a sharp-crested weir springs free from the plate, unless the head is very small. Where the crest is rounded, the liquid tends to adhere to the rounded edge, instead of springing free, and produces a greater discharge.

The discharge through a weir notch is primarily dependent on the head, h, measured from the crest of the weir to the surface of the stream at a distance

*upstream from the weir plate where the surface elevation is not affected by
the flow over the weir.*

9-3 RECTANGULAR WEIR

A commonly used formula for the discharge over a rectangular weir is

$$Q = 3.33(L - 0.1nh)h^{3/2}$$

in which n is the number of end contractions. This formula is called the
Francis formula, modified for end contractions.

Note: The following discussion involves calculus.

The derivation of the Francis formula is as follows:

Write the Bernoulli equation for a streamline of the stream passing
over the weir, as shown in Fig. 9-2, from point 1, upstream from the weir
plate, to point 2, in the nappe just above the weir. Thus,

$$\frac{p_1}{\gamma} + z_1 + \frac{v_1^2}{2g} = \frac{p_2}{\gamma} + -y + \frac{v_2^2}{2g} + h_f. \tag{9-1}$$

The head loss due to friction will be omitted for the present and the velocity
of approach is neglected, assuming the approach channel to be very large
compared to the area of the stream flowing through the weir notch. Therefore, since

$$\frac{p_1}{\gamma} = \frac{p_2}{\gamma},$$

Eq. (9-1) becomes,

$$y = \frac{v_2^2}{2g},$$

and

$$v_2 = (2gy)^{1/2}.$$

If the velocity of the streamlines in the nappe are assumed to be the same
across a horizontal section, the discharge can be expressed as

$$dQ = v_2 \, da = (2gy)^{1/2}x \, dy$$

where $x \, dy$ equals the differential area, da. The total discharge, therefore, is

$$Q = (2g)^{1/2}x \int_0^h y^{1/2} \, dy.$$

Since x varies, but not as a function of y, it is taken outside of the integral. Also, neglecting the vertical contraction of the nappe, the equation becomes

$$Q = \frac{2}{3}(2g)^{1/2}h^{3/2}. \tag{9-2}$$

Equation (9-2) is an expression for the ideal discharge over a weir for which:
1. the velocity of approach is zero,
2. there is no resistance to flow, and
3. there is no vertical contraction of the nappe.

The resistance to flow may be taken into account by introducing the coefficient of velocity, C_v, and the vertical contraction by the coefficient of contraction, C_c. The product of these two coefficients may be expressed as the coefficient of discharge, C_d. Experiments indicate that for a sharp-cornered crest, C_d is approximately 0.622.

An empirical expression for x is

$$x - L - 0.1nh$$

where n is the number of end contractions.

The equation of discharge then becomes

$$Q = 3.33(L - 0.1nh)h^{3/2}. \tag{9-3}$$

The Francis formula gives accurate values of discharge if the head is greater than 0.3 ft and less than one-third the length, L, of the crest of the weir.

Where the ratio of the area of the nappe to the area of the approach channel is large, the velocity of approach can be a factor that must be considered to avoid serious error. This is a primary consideration, especially with suppressed weirs. Where the velocity of approach must be considered, the formula to use is,

$$Q = 3.33(L - 0.1nh)h^{3/2}\left[1 + 0.26\left(\frac{Lh}{a}\right)^2\right]. \tag{9-4}$$

If Lh/a is greater than 0.20, the velocity of approach should be included in the Francis formula.

Example 9-1.   Determine the discharge over a sharp-crested rectangular weir, 8 ft long and 4 ft high, located in the center of a 40 ft channel. The head on the weir is 2.5 ft.

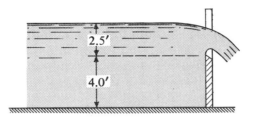

FIGURE 9-3

Solution: Figure 9-3 is a side view of weir and channel, showing the dimensions mentioned in the problem. Since all values necessary to check Lh/a are given, this should be done first. Thus,

$$\frac{Lh}{a} = \frac{8(2.5)}{40(6.5)} = 0.077.$$

Since Lh/a is less than 0.20, the velocity of approach may be neglected. Therefore, using the Francis formula,

$$Q = 3.33[8 - 0.2(2.5)]2.5^{3/2} = 3.33(7.5)4.00 = 100 \text{ cfs.}$$

Example 9-2.   Determine the head on a suppressed rectangular weir, 6 ft long, when the discharge is 25 cfs. The crest of the weir is 4 ft above the bottom of the channel.

Solution: In this problem, Lh/a cannot be evaluated initially. Therefore, assume no velocity of approach in the first trial. Then, using the Francis formula,

$$25 = 3.33(6)h^{3/2}$$

and

$$h = 1.25^{2/3} = 1.16 \text{ ft.}$$

Now, check Lh/a,

$$\frac{Lh}{a} = \frac{6(1.16)}{6(5.16)} = 0.225.$$

Since 0.225 is greater than 0.20, the velocity of approach should be considered. Using the approximate value of h in the modified Francis formula gives

$$25 = 3.33(6)h^{3/2}[1 + 0.26(0.225)^2] = 20.3h^{3/2}.$$

Therefore,

$$h = 1.23^{2/3} = 1.15 \text{ ft.}$$

Since 1.15 is very close to the assumed value of 1.16 used in the evaluation of the velocity of approach, no further computations are necessary. The accepted head is 1.15 ft.

PROBLEMS

9-1. Determine the head on a 5-ft rectangular weir, placed at the center of one side of a large reservoir. The discharge is 20 cfs.

9-2. A rectangular weir, with a crest 3 ft long and 2 ft high, is placed in a rectangular concrete flume that is 5 ft wide. The depth of water in the flume on the upstream side of the weir is 3 ft. Determine the slope of the flume if the flow is uniform. The Manning constant, K, for concrete is 99.

9-3. A rectangular weir, with a crest length of 8 ft, is located in the center of a 12-ft rectangular channel. The height of the weir crest is 3 ft above the floor of the channel. The weir is operating under a head of 1 ft. Determine the discharge over the weir.

9-4. Determine the probable head on a suppressed sharp-edged weir, 5 ft long, when the discharge is 20 cfs. The crest of the weir is 4.5 ft above the bottom of the rectangular channel.

9-5. A rectangular weir, operating under a head of 1 ft, is to be located in the center of a 12-ft rectangular channel. The weir crest is 3 ft above the floor of the channel. If the discharge is to be 25 cfs, determine the length of the weir crest.

9-6. A rectangular weir, operating under a head of 2.0 ft, is to be located in the center of a 40-ft rectangular channel. The weir crest is 5 ft above the floor of the channel. If the discharge is to be 100 cfs, determine the length of the weir crest.

9-7. A rectangular weir, with a crest length of 8 ft, is located in the center of a 12-ft rectangular channel. The height of the weir crest above the floor of the channel is 2 ft and the weir is operating under a head of 1.5 ft. Determine the discharge over the weir.

9-8. Determine the discharge over a rectangular weir, 4 ft long and 1 ft high, placed in the center of a rectangular channel 6 ft wide, if it is operating under a head of 0.5 ft.

9-9. A rectangular weir, with a crest length of 8 ft, is located in the center of a rectangular channel 12 ft wide. The height of the weir crest is 4 ft above the floor of the channel. Determine the upstream depth of the channel when the discharge is 48 cfs.

9-10. Determine the head on a 4-ft rectangular weir placed at the center of one side of a large reservoir, when the discharge is 12 cfs.

9-11. Determine the discharge over a sharp-edged rectangular weir, 8 ft long and 3 ft high, located in the center of a 24-ft rectangular channel, when the head is 2.56 ft.

9-12. Determine the discharge over a suppressed weir 4 ft long under a head of 16 in. The crest of the weir is 9 in. above the bottom of the rectangular channel.

9-13. A rectangular weir, with a crest length of 4 ft, is located at one edge of a rectangular channel 12 ft wide and 5 ft deep. Determine the discharge if the head on the weir is 9 in.

9-14. Water flows 4 ft deep in a rectangular channel that is 16 ft wide. A suppressed weir plate 4 ft high is then placed across the channel and it increases the depth in the channel of approach to 6 ft. Determine the discharge.

9-15. Determine the head on a supressed weir, 8 ft long, when the discharge is 40 cfs. The crest of the weir is 5 ft above the bottom of the rectangular channel.

9-16. Determine the head on a suppressed weir, 2 ft long, when the discharge is 2 cfs. The crest of the weir is 1 ft above the bottom of the rectangular channel.

9-17. An 18-ft rectangular channel carries 180 cfs of water with an average velocity of 4 fps. If an 8-ft rectangular weir, 2 ft high, is installed in the center of the channel, determine the depth of water in the channel of approach.

9-18. A rectangular weir is installed in the center of a 16-ft rectangular channel that carries 80 cfs of water. The weir crest is 2.5 ft above the bottom of the channel. What will be the length of this rectangular weir, if the head on the weir is not to be more than 21 in.?

9-19. A rectangular weir, with a crest length of 3 ft, is built in the center of a rectangular channel 6 ft wide. The crest of the weir is 2 ft above the bottom of the channel. Determine the discharge when the head on the weir is 6 in.

9-20. A rectangular weir 10 ft long is built in the center of one side of a reservoir 100 ft square and 10 ft deep. Water flows into the reservoir and out over the weir at the rate of 100 cfs. Determine the head on the weir.

9-4 TRIANGULAR WEIR

The 90° V-notch, or triangular, weir is commonly used to measure flow rate in a stream or channel. For the sharp-edged 90° triangular weir, good results are obtained by use of the *Thompson formula*, which is

$$Q = 2.54h^{5/2}. \tag{9-5}$$

Note: The following discussion involves calculus.

The Thompson formula can be derived by a method similar to that used to derive the formula for the rectangular weir. Consider the triangular weir in Fig. 9-4. The Bernoulli equation is written from point 1 to point 2 along a

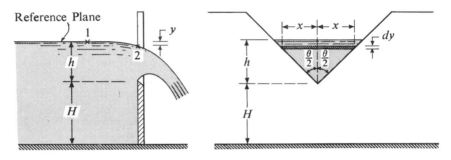

FIGURE 9-4

streamline on the surface of the stream, in which $p_1/\gamma = p_2/\gamma$. The friction loss is omitted and the velocity of approach is neglected, assuming the approach channel to be very large as compared to the cross-sectional area of the stream flowing through the weir notch. Thus,

$$y = \frac{v_2^2}{2g} \quad \text{and} \quad v_2 = (2gy)^{1/2}.$$

Assume the velocity of the streamlines in the nappe to be the same across a horizontal section. The discharge can be expressed as

$$dQ = v_2 \, da = (2gy)^{1/2}2x \, dy,$$

where x may be determined as follows:

$$\tan\frac{\theta}{2} = \frac{x}{h-y} \quad \text{and} \quad 2x = 2(h-y)\tan\frac{\theta}{2}.$$

The ideal discharge becomes,

$$Q = 2\tan\frac{\theta}{2}(2g)^{1/2}\int_0^h (h-y)y^{1/2} \, dy.$$

Integrating and introducing the coefficient C_v to take care of resistance to flow and the coefficient C_c to take care of the contraction at the nappe, the actual discharge becomes,

$$Q = C_v C_c \frac{8}{15} \tan \frac{\theta}{2} (2g)^{1/2} h^{5/2},$$

or

$$Q = K \tan \frac{\theta}{2} h^{5/2}.$$

The coefficient K will vary with the angle $\theta/2$. When θ equals 90°, $\tan \theta/2 = 1$, and K becomes 2.54. Therefore, the equation of discharge for a 90° V-notch weir is

$$Q = 2.54 h^{5/2}.$$

In general, the approach channel, where triangular weirs are installed, is very large as compared to the nappe at the weir notch, therefore the approach velocity can be omitted. Triangular weirs are used primarily for measuring small discharges.

Example 9-3. Determine the discharge over a 90° triangular weir when the head is 4 ft.

Solution: By Eq. (9-5), for a triangular weir,

$$Q = 2.54(4)^{5/2} = 81.3 \text{ cfs.}$$

PROBLEMS

9-21. Determine the head on a 90° triangular weir in a trapezoidal channel. The discharge is 4 cfs of water.

9-22. Determine the discharge over a 90° triangular weir when the head is 15 in.

9-23. Determine the head on a 90° triangular weir that discharges 2 cfs.

9-24. Water flows out of a large tank through several 90° triangular weirs. The vertices of the weirs are at the same elevation. If the discharge varies from 10 to 30 cfs, determine the minimum number of weirs required. The water surface is not to change more than 6 in.

9-25. A 90° triangular weir is discharging water under a head of 15 in. What would be the head on a suppressed rectangular weir 4 ft long and 3 ft high, if it were to replace the triangular weir?

9-26. A rectangular open channel ($K = 124$) is laid on a one percent grade and receives 75 cfs of water from a reservoir over a 90° standard V-notch weir. Determine the most efficient cross section for the channel; and locate the vertex of the weir with respect to the water surface in the reservoir. The water level in the reservoir is to remain at a fixed elevation.

9-27. Determine the head on a 90° triangular weir that is discharging the same quantity of water as would flow through a suppressed rectangular weir 4 ft long and 4 ft high. The head on the rectangular weir is 9 in.

9-28. The discharge from a large tank is regulated by a number of 90° triangular weirs. The weirs are placed in one of the vertical sides. Determine the number of weirs required if the head is not to vary more than 0.50 ft when the discharge varies from 1 to 6 cfs. The vertices of the weirs are at the same elevation.

9-29. Determine the head on a 90° triangular weir when the discharge is 4 cfs.

9-30. Determine the required head on a 90° triangular weir in order to give the same discharge as an 8.0-ft rectangular weir that is operating under a head of 1.0 ft. The rectangular weir is 2 ft high and it is centered in a channel 12 ft wide.

9-31. Determine the discharge over a 90° triangular weir under a head of 4 ft.

9-32. Water flows from a reservoir over a 90° triangular weir into a rectangular flume ($K = 50$) which is laid on a slope of 0.16 percent. Determine the required dimensions of the flume if the water velocity is to be 2 fps when the head on the weir is 2.5 ft.

9-33. Water is supplied to a reservoir at a varying rate and discharges through several 90° triangular weirs. The vertices of all the weirs are at the same elevation. If it is desired to vary the discharge from 200 to 100 cfs without having the level of the water surface change more than 1 ft, determine the minimum number of weirs required.

9-34. The discharge over several sharp-crested 90° triangular weirs varies from 25.4 cfs to 143.5 cfs. Determine the minimum number of weirs required if the change in head is not to exceed 1 ft.

9-35. Five 90° triangular weirs and a sharp-edged rectangular weir, 3 ft long, are placed in the side of a large reservoir. The bottom of the notches and the crest of the rectangular weir are on the same level. Determine the head that must be maintained to cause the total discharge over the five V-notch weirs to equal the discharge over the rectangular weir.

9-36. Water is discharged from a large reservoir at the rate of 50 cfs through a 90° triangular weir. The discharge from the weir is carried by a rectangular channel that is laid on a 1 percent slope. Determine **(a)** the head on the weir, and **(b)** the least dimensions of the most efficient cross section of the channel. ($K = 65$.)

9-37. Water, flowing into a large channel, discharges over several 90° triangular weirs. If the discharge varies from 5 to 10 cfs and the head on the weirs is not to vary more than 3 in., determine the number of weirs required. The vertices of all the weirs are on the same level.

9-38. A 90° triangular weir in the side of a large reservoir, discharging water under a head of 2.25 ft, is to be replaced by a 4-ft rectangular weir. What will be the head on the rectangular weir in order to give the same discharge as the triangular weir?

9-39. A 4-ft sharp-crested rectangular weir and a 90° triangular weir are placed in the side of a reservoir. Determine the necessary vertical distance from the bottom of the triangular weir to the crest of the rectangular weir in order that the discharge over each weir will be the same when the head on the rectangular weir is 0.80 ft. Neglect velocity of approach.

9-40. A 90° triangular weir discharges water from a large reservoir under a head of 3 ft. What should be the diameter of a standard short tube located 25 ft below the surface of the reservoir to give the same discharge?

9-41. Determine the required head on a 90° triangular weir to give the same discharge as an 8 ft rectangular weir, operating under a head of 1 ft. The rectangular weir is 2 ft high and it is centered in a channel 12 ft wide.

9-5   CIPOLLETTI WEIR

The Cipolletti weir is a trapezoidal weir for which the sides of the notch have a slope of 4 to 1. See Fig. 9-5. In a sense, it is a combination of a rectangular

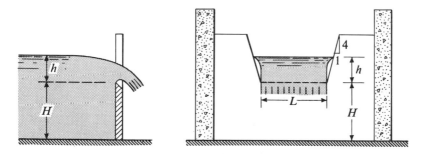

FIGURE 9-5

weir with the two halves of a triangular weir having side slopes of 4 to 1 placed at the ends. The slope of the sides eliminates end contraction in the Francis formula, so that, assuming C_d equals 0.622, the equation becomes,

$$Q = 3.33Lh^{3/2}, \qquad (9\text{-}6)$$

which is the same as the formula for a suppressed weir. Again, the head should not be less than 0.30 feet nor greater than one-third the length of the crest of the weir for good results.

Example 9-4.   Determine the head necessary for a 9-ft Cipolletti weir, which is placed near the center of a 30-ft channel, to discharge 75 cfs. The crest of the weir is 3 ft above the bottom of the channel.

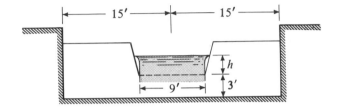

FIGURE 9-6

Solution: Figure 9-6 is a sketch of the weir. Since the head, h, is unknown, the velocity of approach cannot be immediately computed. First, determine the approximate head. By Eq. (9-6),

$$Q = 3.33Lh^{3/2}.$$

Therefore,

$$h = \left[\frac{75}{3.33(9)}\right]^{2/3} = 1.842 \text{ ft.}$$

Checking Lh/a,

$$\frac{Lh}{a} = \frac{9(1.842)}{30(4.842)} = 0.114$$

Since 0.114 is less than 0.20, the velocity of approach may be neglected and the head, h, is 1.842 feet on the Cipolletti weir.

9-6   OTHER WEIR FORMULAS

Weir formulas usually have certain limitations. New weir formulas should be used with caution until their limitations are discovered. The Francis formula is recommended when the head is not greater than one-third the length of the crest. For a suppressed weir, the formula $Q = 3.10Lh^{3/2}$ may be used when the head is equal to or greater than the crest length.

The Bazin formula, which applies to suppressed weirs over a large range of heads, is

$$Q = \left[3.248 + \frac{0.0789}{h}\, Lh^{3/2}\left[1 + 0.55\left(\frac{h}{d}\right)^2\right]\right],$$

where d is the depth of the stream on the approach side of the weir plate.

The King formula, also used for suppressed weirs, is

$$Q = \left[3.34Lh^{1.47}\left[1 + 0.56\left(\frac{h}{d}\right)^2\right]\right].$$

Two other formulas, which give the discharge over the sharp-edged 90° triangular weirs, are:

The Barr formula, $Q = 2.48h^{2.48}$;

The Michigan formula, $Q = 2.52h^{2.47}$.

PROBLEMS

9-42. A Cipolletti weir is placed in the vertical side of a large reservoir. Determine the length of the weir if the head varies 0.4 ft as the discharge changes from 10 to 20 cfs.

9-43. A Cipolletti weir with a crest length of 3 ft, discharging under a head 12 in., is to be replaced by a 90° triangular weir. For the same discharge, what will be the head on the triangular weir?

9-44. A Cipolletti weir is placed in the vertical side of a large reservoir. Determine the length of the weir if the head varies 3 in. as the discharge varies from 6 to 12 cfs.

9-45. Determine the head on a 9-ft Cipolletti weir when the discharge is 72 cfs. The crest of the weir is 4 ft above the bottom and it is near the center of a 22-ft channel.

9-46. A Cipolletti weir is placed in the vertical side of a large tank. When the discharge varies from 10 to 30 cfs, the head varies 0.75 ft. Determine the length of the crest of the weir.

9-47. A Cipolletti weir is placed in the center of a wide channel in which the discharge varies from 25 cfs to 75 cfs. What minimum length of weir is required if the head is not to vary more than 1.25 ft.

9-48. Water is discharged from a large reservoir at the rate of 150 cfs through a 15 ft Cipolletti weir. The discharge from the weir is carried by a rectangular channel ($K = 42$) that is laid on a one percent slope.

Determine (a) the head on the weir, and (b) the minimum width of the channel if the depth is not to exceed 4 ft.

9-49. A Cipolletti weir is to be placed in a rectangular channel 18 feet wide. The channel carries a maximum discharge of 120 cfs and a minimum discharge of 90 cfs. Determine the length of the weir if the depth of the water in the channel is not to vary more than ± 3 in. from 10 ft.

9-50. A Cipolletti weir, operating under a head of 1.5 ft, is to be located at the center of a 30 ft channel with the crest 4 ft above the floor of the channel. If the discharge is to be 100 cfs, determine the length of the weir crest.

9-51. A Cipolletti weir, with a crest length of 12 ft, is placed in the side of a large reservoir in such a position that the head on it is 3 ft. How many 90° triangular weirs would be required to give the same discharge if their vertices are placed 15 in. below the crest of the Cipolletti weir?

9-52. A 10-ft Cipolletti weir is to discharge water under a maximum head of 2 ft from a large reservoir into an open channel having the most efficient rectangular cross section. If the slope of the channel is 0.81 ft/100 ft, and $n = 0.015$, determine the base width and depth of the channel.

9-53. A 3-ft Cipolletti weir in the side of a large reservoir discharges water under a head of 1 ft. If it is replaced with a 90° triangular weir and gives the same discharge, determine the head on the triangular weir.

9-54. Water is to be discharged from a large irrigation canal at the rate of 10 cfs through a Cipolletti weir under a head of 0.81 ft into an open channel that is laid on a slope of 0.90 ft/1000 ft. Determine (a) the length of the weir crest, and (b) the least dimensions of the most efficient cross section for a rectangular channel. Assume the friction coefficient, K, equal to 100.

9-55. An 8-ft Cipolletti weir is to discharge water under a maximum head of 2.25 ft from a large reservoir into an open rectangular channel that has the most efficient cross section. If the slope of the channel is 6.4 ft/1000 ft, and $K = 100$, determine the minimum dimensions of the channel.

9-56. Solve Prob. 9-4, using the King formula.

9-57. Solve Prob. 9-12, using the Bazin formula.

9-58. Solve Prob. 9-15, using the King formula.

9-59. Solve Prob. 9-16, using the Bazin formula.

Chapter 10

Variable Flow

10-1 DISCHARGE UNDER FALLING HEAD

Often a situation may arise where it becomes necessary to fill or drain a tank or reservoir. The time required to fill or empty a container under a varying head may become a matter of considerable importance. This problem may be solved by equating the volume of liquid lost from a tank or container per unit of time to the volume discharged through the opening from the container.

In order to determine accurately the time necessary to empty a tank, without resorting to calculus, the liquid in the tank can be divided into a great number of very thin horizontal layers. The summation of the time for each layer to be discharged results in the total time required to empty the tank. However, this method is very time consuming. An approximation of the time required to empty a tank may be determined by dividing a tank of liquid into a smaller number of layers of finite thicknesses, for example, 1 ft thicknesses, and adding the time necessary to discharge each layer. The head for each layer can be taken to the centroid of the layer. Of course, the greater the number of layers into which the liquid is divided, the more accurate is the result.

Example 10-1. The cylindrical tank, shown in Fig. 10-1(a), is 4 ft in diameter and has a 2-in.-diameter standard short tube provided to lower the water level. Determine the time required to lower the water level in the tank from 9 ft to 4 ft above the tube.

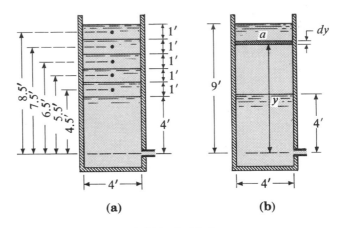

(a)   (b)

FIGURE 10-1

Solution: Let the tank in Fig. 10-1(a) be divided into layers 1 ft thick. The volume of each layer is 4(3.14)1, or 12.56 cu ft. The head, h, for each layer is 8.5, 7.5, 6.5, 5.5, and 4.5 ft, respectively. The discharge through the 2-in.-diameter short tube is

$$Q = 0.82 \frac{3.14}{144} (2gh)^{1/2} = 0.143h^{1/2}.$$

Therefore,
$$0.143h^{1/2}t = 12.56$$

and

$$t = \frac{87.8}{h^{1/2}}.$$

For
$$h = 8.5 \text{ ft, } t = 30.1 \text{ sec}$$
$$h = 7.5 \text{ ft, } t = 32.1 \text{ sec}$$
$$h = 6.5 \text{ ft, } t = 34.5 \text{ sec}$$
$$h = 5.5 \text{ ft, } t = 37.4 \text{ sec}$$

and
$$h = 4.5 \text{ ft, } t = 41.3 \text{ sec.}$$

The total time is 175.4 sec.

Note: The following discussion involves calculus.

Problems of falling head may be solved by setting up a differential equation in terms of the volume of liquid lost from a tank and the volume of liquid discharged per unit of time, and integrating between the limits of the liquid levels. Consider Fig. 10-1(b). Select the origin at the center of the outlet with y positive upward. The loss of volume of the liquid in the tank in time, dt, is

$$dQ = -a\,dy,$$

in which a is the area of the surface of the liquid. The negative sign is necessary since dy is measured downward although y is positive upward.

The volume of liquid that is discharged through an orifice, short tube, weir, or closed pipe in time dt is

$$dQ = Q\,dt.$$

Since the loss in the tank and the discharge are the same,

$$-a\,dy = Q\,dt. \tag{10-1}$$

Applying Eq. (10-1) to the tank in Fig. 10-1(b), the falling head equation becomes

$$-\pi 2^2\,dy = 0.82\,\frac{\pi}{144}\,(64.4)^{1/2}y^{1/2}\,dt$$

and

$$-\pi 2^2 \int_9^4 y^{-1/2}\,dy = 0.82\,\frac{\pi}{144}\,(8.03)\int_0^t dt$$

and

$$-2(12.56)(2-3) = 0.143t$$

$$t = 175.7 \text{ sec}$$

Example 10-2.   A tank is formed as a volume of revolution described by revolving the curve having equation $2x^2 = 3y$, about the y axis. Both x and y are measured in feet. Determine the time required to lower the water level in the tank from 16 ft to 9 ft if there is a 3-in.-diameter standard orifice located in the bottom of the tank, as shown in Fig. 10-2.

Solution: In the equation, $-a\,dy = Q\,dt$, $a = \pi x^2 = (\pi 3y)/2$, and

$$Q = 0.60\,\frac{\pi}{64}\,(8.03)y^{1/2}.$$

Therefore,

$$\frac{-3\pi}{2} \int_{16}^{9} y^{1/2} \, dy = 0.60 \frac{\pi}{64} (8.03) \int_{0}^{t} dt$$

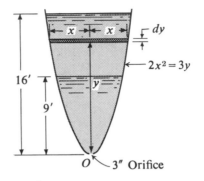

FIGURE 10-2

Integrating,

$$-y^{3/2} \int_{16}^{9} = 0.0753t \int_{0}^{t}$$

Therefore,

$$-(27 - 64) = 0.0753t$$

and

$$t = 492 \text{ sec, or } 8 \text{ min, } 12 \text{ sec.}$$

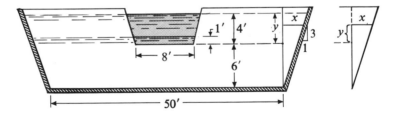

FIGURE 10-3

Example 10-3. The end view of a large reservoir, which has vertical ends and is 100 ft long, is shown in Fig. 10-3. An 8-ft Cipolletti weir is located at one end of the reservoir. Determine the value of the discharge coefficient for the weir if the head on the weir changes from 4 ft to 1 ft in 6½ minutes.

Solution: First, determine the area of the water surface in terms of the head, y. Referring to Fig. 10-3,

$$\frac{x}{6+y} = \frac{1}{3} \quad \text{or} \quad x = \frac{6+y}{3} = 2 + \frac{y}{3}.$$

Therefore, the area, a, is,

$$a = 100(50 + 2x) = 100 \left(50 + 4 + \frac{2y}{3}\right) = 100 \left(54 + \frac{2y}{3}\right).$$

Also, the equation for the discharge over a Cipolletti weir, with the coefficient unknown, is $Q = KLh^{3/2}$; therefore, since

$$-a\, dy = Q\, dt,$$

$$-100 \left(54 + \frac{2y}{3}\right) dy = K(8)y^{3/2}\, dt$$

and

$$-100 \int_4^1 54y^{-3/2}\, dy - \frac{200}{3} \int_4^1 y^{-1/2}\, dy = 8K \int_0^t dt.$$

Integrating,

$$\frac{-100(108)}{y^{1/2}} \Big|_4^1 - \frac{400}{3} y^{1/2} \Big|_4^1 = K8t \Big|_0^{390}.$$

Then,

$$\frac{-100(108)}{1-2} - \frac{400}{3}(1 - 2) = 3120K,$$

and

$$K = \frac{10{,}800 + 133}{3120} = \frac{10{,}933}{3120} = 3.50$$

PROBLEMS

10-1. The square tank, shown in Fig. P 10-1, is 4 ft square and has a 2-in.-diameter standard orifice in the bottom of the tank that is used to lower the water level. How much time is required to lower the water level in the tank 7 ft, if the original depth of the water is 16 ft.

10-2. The 3-in.-diameter standard short tube, placed in the bottom of the circular tank in Fig. P 10-2, has a discharge coefficient of 0.82.

Determine the time necessary for the water to drop from a depth of 9 ft to 4 ft when the tube is flowing full.

10-3. The standard short tube in Fig. P 10-3 is 2 in. in diameter and C_c and C_v are 1.00 and 0.82, respectively. If the water level in the 4-ft diameter tank initially is 9 ft above the center of the tube, how long, in seconds, will it take for the discharge through the short tube to lower the water level 5 ft?

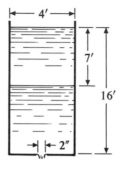

FIGURE P 10-1

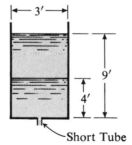

FIGURE P 10-2

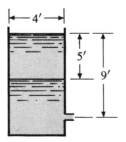

FIGURE P 10-3

10-4.   The end view of a tank, which has vertical ends and is 10 ft long, is shown in Fig. P 10-4. Determine the time required to lower the head from 16 ft to 4 ft by means of the 3-in.-diameter standard orifice in the bottom of the tank.

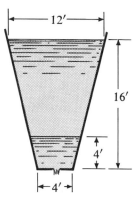

FIGURE P 10-4

10-5.   A 2-in.-diameter standard short tube in the side of a circular tank, as shown in Fig. P 10-5, discharges water for a period of 5 minutes. If the water level is initially 12 ft above the bottom of the tank, determine the water level at the end of the discharge period.

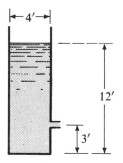

FIGURE P 10-5

10-6.   A tank, 12 ft long, having the cross section shown in Fig. P 10-6, and vertical ends, has a 2-in. standard short tube, $(C_d = 0.80)$ located in the bottom. The water level initially is 9 ft above the bottom of the tank. Determine the time required for the water level to drop to 4 ft above the bottom of the tank.

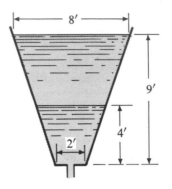

FIGURE P 10-6

10-7.   A 20-ft square reservoir with vertical sides discharges water through a 5-ft Cipolletti weir. The expression for the discharge over the weir is $Q = KLh^{3/2}$, where Q is in cfs, h is in ft, L is in ft, and K is a constant. Determine the value and units of K if the head on the weir changes from 1.44 ft to 1.00 ft in 8 sec.

10-8.   The end view of a tank, which has vertical ends and is 6 ft long, is shown in Fig. P 10-8. A standard 1-in.-diameter short tube discharges water from the bottom of the tank. Determine the time required to lower the head from 4 ft to 1 ft above the bottom of the tank.

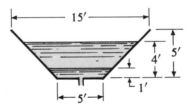

FIGURE P 10-8

10-9.   A 40-ft long by 10-ft wide reservoir with vertical sides discharges water through a 4-ft Cipolletti weir. The expression for the discharge over the weir is $Q = KLh^{3/2}$, where Q is in cfs, h is in ft, L is the crest length in ft, and K is a constant. Determine the value and units of K if the head on the weir changes from 1 ft to 0.5 ft in 25 sec.

10-10.   The end view of a tank, which has vertical ends and is 10 ft long, is shown in Fig. P 10-10. A standard orifice 2 in. in diameter is placed in the bottom of the tank. Initially, the head is 9 ft above the bottom of the tank. Determine the time required to lower the head to 4 ft above the bottom of the tank.

10-11. The end view of a tank, which has vertical ends and is 10 ft long, is shown in Fig. P 10-11. A 2-in.-diameter orifice is located in the bottom of the tank. Determine the value of the discharge coefficient for the orifice, if the head on the orifice changes from 9 ft to 4 ft in 20 min.

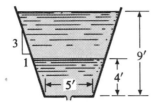

FIGURE P 10-10

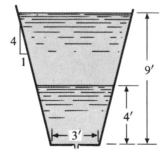

FIGURE P 10-11

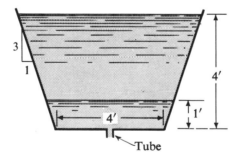

FIGURE P 10-12

10-12. The end view of a tank, which has vertical ends and is 15 ft long, is shown in Fig. P 10-12. A 3-in.-diameter tube is located in the bottom of the tank. Determine the value of the discharge coefficient for the tube, which is assumed to run full, if the head on the orifice changes from 4 ft to 1 ft in 10 minutes.

10-13. A tank is formed as a volume of revolution described by revolving the curve having the equation $x^2 = 4y$ about the y axis, as shown in Fig. P 10-13. Both x and y are measured in ft. Determine the time required to lower the level of water in the tank from 18 ft to 6 ft, if there is a 3-in. standard orifice located in the bottom of the tank at the origin.

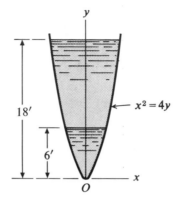

FIGURE P 10-13

10-14. Determine the time required to empty half of a spherical tank that is full of oil ($S_g = 0.85$). The oil will be discharged through a 2-in. opening having the same coefficient of discharge as a standard short tube. The opening is placed as shown in Fig. P 10-14.

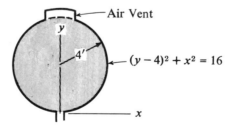

FIGURE P 10-14

10-15. A tank, 10 ft long having vertical ends and a cross section as shown in Fig. P 10-15, has a 2-in. standard orifice located in the bottom. Initially, the water level is 4 ft above the bottom of the tank. Determine the time required for the water level to drop to 2 ft above the bottom of the tank.

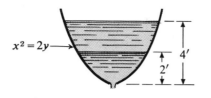

FIGURE P 10-15

Chapter *11*

Forces Produced by
Fluids in Motion

11-1 INTRODUCTION

The forces produced by fluids in motion affect the design of pumps, turbines, pipe bends, and changes in cross sections of pipes and channels.

The general equation best adapted to this type of problem is the equation of linear impulse and momentum,

$$\sum \mathbf{F}_x t = M(\bar{v}_{f_x} - \bar{v}_{i_x})$$

where $\bar{v}_{f_x}$ is the final velocity, or component of final velocity, of the fluid in the x direction, and

$\bar{v}_{i_x}$ is the initial velocity, or component of initial velocity, in the x direction.

When both sides of the equation are divided by t, the equation becomes

$$\sum \mathbf{F}_x = \frac{M}{t}(\bar{v}_{f_x} - \bar{v}_{i_x})$$

where $\mathbf{F}_x$ = the summation of the x components of all forces acting,
M/t = the mass of fluid that has its velocity changed per unit of time, ρQ.

In the same way, similar equations may be developed in the y and z directions. The equations are applied to free-body diagrams of the fluid, as shown in the following examples.

Example 11-1.   A jet of water, 2-in. in diameter, having an initial velocity of 100 fps, strikes a stationary curved vane which deflects the jet through a horizontal angle of 60°, as shown in Fig. 11-1. Neglect any frictional resistance between the water and the vane. Determine the force that the water exerts on the vane.

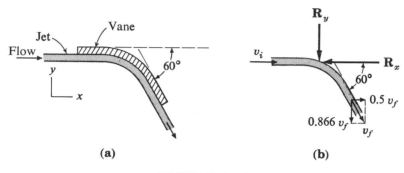

(a)   (b)

FIGURE 11-1

Solution: Figure 11-1(b) is the free-body diagram of the jet being deflected by the vane. The resultant components of the reaction of the vane on the jet in the x and y directions are shown. Since friction is neglected, the magnitude of the final velocity of the jet is the same as the magnitude of the initial velocity of the jet.

     Substituting values into the impulse and momentum equation gives

$$-R_x = 100 \, \frac{\pi}{144} \, 1.94[0.5(100) - 100] = 4.22(-50) = -211 \text{ lb.}$$

Therefore, $R_x = 211$ lb $\leftarrow$, which is the reaction of the vane on the jet of water in the x direction. In a similar way,

$$R_y = 4.22[0.866(100) - 0] = 0.422(86.6) = 365 \text{ lb } \downarrow,$$

which is the reaction of the vane on the jet of water in the y direction. The resultant of these two components is

$$R = (211^2 + 365^2)^{1/2} = 422 \text{ lb } {}_{211}\!\!\diagup^{365}.$$

Therefore, the resultant force of the water on the vane is 422 lb ${}_{211}\!\!\diagup^{365}$.

Example 11-2. Assume that the vane in Ex. 11-1 moves to the right with a uniform velocity of 40 fps. Determine the resultant components of the force in the x and y directions exerted by the vane on the water.

Solution: The mass of water deflected per second is now determined from the relative velocity of the jet with respect to the vane. That is,

$$v_{i_r} = v_j - v_v = 100 - 40 = 60 \text{ fps}$$

where v_{i_r} = the initial relative velocity of the jet with respect to the vane,

v_j = the initial absolute velocity of the jet, and

v_v = the absolute velocity of the vane.

Since friction is neglected, the relative velocity of the jet with respect to the vane as it leaves the vane is still 60 fps. Therefore, using the impulse and momentum equation, gives,

$$-\mathbf{R}_x = 60 \frac{\pi}{144} 1.94[0.5(60) - 60] = 2.539(-30) = -76.2 \text{ lb.}$$

and

$$\mathbf{R}_x = 76.2 \text{ lb} \leftarrow.$$

Using the same equation,

$$\mathbf{R}_y = 2.539[0.866(60) - 0] = 2.535(52) = 131.9 \text{ lb} \downarrow.$$

The components of the resultant force exerted by the vane on the water in the x and y directions, therefore, are 76.2 lb $\leftarrow$ and 131.9 lb $\downarrow$.

Example 11-3. Again, assume the vane in Ex. 11-1 moves to the right with a uniform velocity of 40 fps, but the final relative velocity of the jet with respect to the vane is reduced by friction to 80 percent of its initial relative velocity. Determine the components of the force exerted by the vane on the water in the x and y directions.

Solution: All values will remain the same as in Ex. 11-2 except the final relative velocity, which will be 0.80(60), or 48 fps. Therefore,

$$-\mathbf{R}_x = 2.539[0.5(48) - 60] = 2.539(-36) = -91.4 \text{ lb}$$

and

$$\mathbf{R}_x = 91.4 \text{ lb} \leftarrow.$$

Also,

$$\mathbf{R}_y = 2.539[0.866(48) - 0) = 2.539(41.6) = 105.5 \text{ lb} \downarrow.$$

Therefore, the components, $\mathbf{R}_x$ and $\mathbf{R}_y$, computed above, are the components of the force exerted by the vane on the water in the x and y directions.

PROBLEMS

11-1.   A 2-in. jet of water at 68°F, traveling with a velocity of 60 fps, strikes a fixed plate, the plane of which is normal to the jet. Determine the force exerted by the water on the plate.

11-2.   A jet of water, 1-in. in diameter and having a velocity of 30 fps, strikes a stationary plate, as shown in Fig. P 11-2. Determine the resultant force exerted by the water on the plate.

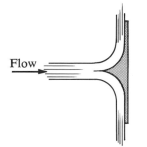

FIGURE P 11-2

11-3.   If the plate in Prob. 11-2 is moving in the same direction as the initial velocity of the jet and with a uniform velocity of 15 fps, determine the resultant force exerted by the water on the plate.

11-4.   A 2-in. jet of water, with a velocity of 100 fps, strikes a stationary vane having a deflection angle of 165°. Determine the resultant force that the water exerts on the vane. Neglect friction between the water and the vane.

11-5.   In Prob. 11-4, assume that the vane moves in the direction of the jet at 40 fps. Determine the component of the resultant force exerted by the water on the vane in the direction of the jet.

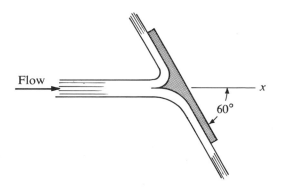

FIGURE P 11-6

11-6. A 1-in. jet of water at 59°F, having a velocity of 80 fps, strikes the stationary single vane in Fig. P 11-6. The vane splits the jet exactly in half. Determine the component of the resultant force exerted by the water on the vane in the x direction. Neglect friction.

11-7. A 2-in. jet of water, having a velocity of 50 fps, is deflected through an angle of 60° by a fixed curved vane. Determine the component of the force exerted by the water on the vane in the initial direction of the jet.

11-8. Solve Prob. 11-6 if the vane is moving in the initial direction of the jet at 30 fps.

11-9. Solve Prob. 11-6 if the vane is moving directly against the initial direction of the jet at 30 fps.

11-10. A 2-in. jet of water having a velocity of 60 fps in the x direction is deflected through an angle of 60° by a vane that is moving with a velocity of 24 fps in the same direction as the initial velocity of the jet. Determine the x and y components of the force exerted by the water on the vane.

11-11. A 2-in. nozzle having a coefficient of contraction of 0.90 discharges 1 cfs. Determine the force required to move a single flat plate toward the nozzle with a velocity of 12 fps if the jet of water impinges normally on the plate.

11-12. A single flat plate is moved at a velocity of 8 fps toward a nozzle, which is discharging 50 gpm of water with a velocity of 24 fps. The jet strikes normally to the plate. Determine (a) the force exerted by the jet on the plate, and (b) the rate, in gpm, at which the water strikes the plate.

11-2 WORK DONE ON MOVING VANES

Since work is the product of force and distance, the work done by a jet on a vane is $\mathbf{F}d$, where $\mathbf{F}$ is the force of the jet on the vane in the direction of the motion of the vane, and d is the distance travelled by the vane. The work done per unit of time is power and is equal to $\mathbf{F}v_v$, where v_v is the velocity of the vane. Therefore, since one horsepower is equal to 550 ft-lb of work per second, the horsepower due to a force acting on a moving vane is

$$\text{hp} = \frac{\mathbf{F}v_v}{550}$$

in which $\mathbf{F}$ = the force acting on the vane, lb; and

v_v = the velocity of the vane, fps.

Where a series of vanes are acted upon by a jet, as in the case of a Pelton impulse wheel, all the fluid of the jet is deflected; that is, as one vane recedes, another takes its place in the path of the jet. Therefore the force equation becomes,

$$-\mathbf{R}_x = \frac{M}{t}\,(v_{f_r} - v_{i_r}) = v_j a \rho(v_{f_r} - v_{i_r})$$

where v_{f_r} and v_{i_r} are the final and initial relative velocities of the jet with respect to the vane, and

M is the total mass of fluid leaving the nozzle per second, which is also the total mass of fluid being deflected by the vanes per second.

Figure 11-2(a) is a sketch of a Pelton impulse wheel. Figure 11-2(b) shows the cross section of one of the buckets, or vanes, of the wheel, and points out the action of the jet on the vane. Figure 11-2(c) is

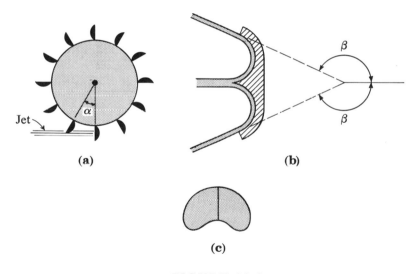

FIGURE 11-2

the projection of the lowest vane on a vertical plane and shows the notch at the bottom of the vane. This notch permits the vane to move very closely to its lowest point before the jet strikes it. This reduces the angle α (Fig. 11-2(a)) to a minimum so that the energy lost due to the reaction of the jet on the vane in the direction of the axle of the wheel becomes negligible in the development of the power of the wheel.

The angle β, which is the angle between the relative velocity of the water as it leaves the vane and the direction of motion of the vane, is the deflection angle of the vane. See Fig. 11-2(b). Theoretically, the maximum efficiency of the wheel would be obtained when $\beta = 180°$. However, this is not practical because the water leaving the vanes would interfere with the motion of the next vane to be acted upon by the jet. Therefore, the angle is made slightly less than 180° in order to bring the emerging water away from the vanes.

As the peripheral velocity of the wheel changes from zero to a maximum, the power developed by the wheel also changes. When the wheel is at rest the power is zero since v_v, in the product $\mathbf{F}v_v$ is zero. Also, if the wheel is allowed to travel at approximately the speed of the jet, the power is again approximately zero since $\mathbf{F}$, in the product $\mathbf{F}v_v$, is a minimum. Somewhere between these extremes the wheel operates at its maximum efficiency. If hydraulic and mechanical losses are neglected, this is where the velocity of the wheel is one-half the velocity of the jet. Hydraulic losses are those due to angles α and β. Hydraulic losses are due to the friction of the jet on the vanes. Mechanical losses are those due to bearing friction of the wheel and windage due to the rotating wheel. The overall efficiency is the product of the hydraulic and mechanical efficiencies. Therefore, because of fluid friction, α not being zero and β not being 180°, also because of windage and bearing friction, the ratio of the velocity of the vane to the velocity of jet for maximum efficiency will fall between 0.43 and 0.47. This ratio is called the *speed factor*.

Example 11-4.   The following data apply to a Pelton impulse wheel:

Diameter of jet	2 in.
Diameter of wheel	2 ft
Velocity of jet	100 fps
Velocity of vane	44 fps
Bucket deflection angle	165°

Determine the horsepower developed and the hydraulic efficiency. Neglect friction.

Solution: Figure 11-3 shows the action of the jet on one of the buckets of the wheel. Cosine 165° = 0.9659. The relative velocity of the jet with respect to the vane is

$$v_j - v_v = 100 - 44 = 56 \text{ fps.}$$

Substituting into the impulse and momentum equation gives

$$-\mathbf{R}_x = 100\,\frac{\pi}{144}\,1.94[-0.9659(56) - 56]$$

$$-\mathbf{R}_x = 4.22[-54.1 - 56] = 4.22(-110.1) = -465\ \text{lb}$$

and

$$\text{hp} = \frac{F_v}{550} = \frac{465(44)}{550} = 37.2\ \text{hp.}$$

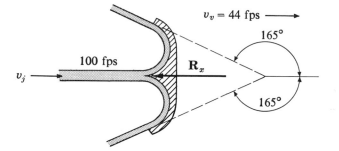

$v_v = 44$ fps

165°

100 fps $\mathbf{R}_x$

v_j

165°

FIGURE 11-3

The hydraulic efficiency can be determined by computing the power input into the wheel. Thus,

$$\text{power input} = \tfrac{1}{2}Mv_j^2 = \tfrac{1}{2}(4.22)100^2 = 21{,}100\ \text{ft-lb/sec.}$$

and

$$\text{horsepower input} = \frac{21{,}000}{550} = 38.4\ \text{hp.}$$

Therefore,

$$\text{hydraulic efficiency} = \frac{37.2(100)}{38.4} = 96.9\ \text{percent.}$$

Example 11-5.   In Ex. 11-4, assume the Pelton wheel delivers 35 horsepower. Determine the overall efficiency of the wheel.

Solution: The horsepower delivered by the jet, as computed in Ex. 11-4, is 38.4, therefore,

$$\text{overall efficiency} = \frac{35.0(100)}{38.4} = 91.1\ \text{percent.}$$

PROBLEMS

11-13. The following data apply to a certain impulse wheel:

Diameter of jet	3 in.
Diameter of wheel	3 ft
Speed of wheel	360 rpm
Bucket deflection angle	150°

Determine the required velocity of the jet of water if the wheel is to develop 175 hp. Neglect friction.

11-14. The following data apply to an impulse wheel:

Diameter of jet	4 in.
Diameter of wheel	4 ft
Speed of wheel	390 rpm
Bucket deflection angle	150°

Determine the required velocity of the jet of water if the wheel is to develop 720 hp. Neglect friction.

11-15. A 4-ft diameter impulse wheel is operated at a speed of 300 rpm. The diameter of the entering jet of water is 4 in. and the velocity of the jet is 140 fps. The bucket deflection angle is 150°, the mechanical efficiency of the turbine is 90 percent. Fluid friction may be neglected. Determine the horsepower output of the wheel.

11-16. A Pelton wheel, having buckets with a 150° deflection angle, is operated at a speed factor of 0.40. The nozzle coefficient, C_v, is 0.97, and the total head at the base of the nozzle is 81 ft of water. $C_c = 1.00$. Neglect friction. Determine the percent of the energy in the jet that is transmitted to the wheel.

11-17. A 4-ft diameter impulse wheel is operated at a speed of 260 rpm. The diameter of the entering jet of water is 4-in., the bucket deflection angle is 150°, and the output of the wheel is 300 hp. Assume the mechanical efficiency of the impulse sheet to be 90 percent. Neglect fluid friction. Determine the velocity of the jet.

11-18. A 3-in. jet supplies water to an impulse wheel that has a diameter of 3-ft and a bucket deflection angle of 165°. When the wheel operates with a speed factor of 0.42 it develops 80 hp. Determine the velocity of the jet as it strikes the wheel. Neglect friction.

11-19. The following data apply to a certain water impulse wheel:

Diameter of jet	2 in.
Diameter of wheel	2 ft
Velocity of jet	100 fps
Bucket deflection angle	150°

When the wheel is operating at the most efficient theoretical speed, what horsepower is developed?

11-20. Water is supplied to a 2-ft diameter impulse wheel through a 4-in. by 2-in. nozzle for which C_v is 0.93 and C_c is 1.00. The bucket deflection angle is 150°. If the velocity of the jet is 80 fps and the wheel is operating at the most efficient theoretical speed, determine **(a)** the horsepower developed, and **(b)** the pressure at the base of the nozzle. Neglect friction.

11-21. The following data apply to a certain impulse wheel:

Diameter of jet	2 in.
Diameter of wheel	2 ft
Velocity of wheel	450 rpm
Bucket deflection angle	150°
Horsepower developed	36

Determine the probable velocity of the jet as it strikes the blades.

11-22. A 2-in. jet of water at 68°F, travelling with a velocity of 60 fps, strikes a flat plate, the plane of which is normal to the jet, travelling in the direction of the jet at 20 fps. Determine the horsepower delivered to the plate.

11-23. A 2-in. jet of water, with a velocity of 100 fps, strikes a single vane having a deflection angle of 165° and moving in the direction of the jet at 40 fps. Determine the horsepower developed by the vane.

11-24. The cusped vanes on a 4-ft-diameter impulse wheel are curved through an arc of 160°. The wheel is driven at a speed of 220 rpm by a 2-in. jet of water having a velocity of 120 ft/sec. Compute the force on the vanes and the horsepower developed.

11-3 APPLICATIONS TO PIPES

As water flows through pipes, transverse stresses are set up due to the internal pressure. Also, as the flow is deflected in various directions or when the pipe size converges or diverges, additional reaction forces are set up producing tension or compression in the pipe. These forces can be evaluated in a manner similar to that used for stationary vanes, with the exception that the pressure in the fluid in a closed pipe is no longer zero. The free-body diagram of the fluid passing through a 45° bend is shown in Fig. 11-4,

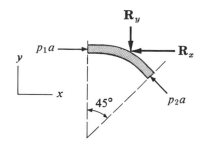

FIGURE 11-4

where p_1 = the pressure at the inlet to the bend, psi
          p_2 = the pressure at the outlet of the bend, psi
          $\mathbf{R}_x$ = the x component of the reaction of the bend on the water, lb
          $\mathbf{R}_y$ = the y component of the reaction of the bend on the water, lb
          a = the cross-sectional area of the flowing fluid, $in.^2$.

The impulse and momentum equation then becomes,

$$-\mathbf{R}_x + p_1 a_1 - p_2 a_2 \cos \theta = \frac{M}{t}(v_f - v_i).$$

Example 11-6. Determine the rectangular components of the resultant fluid force on a 60° bend, located in a horizontal 12-in. pipe line, which is discharging 7.85 cfs of water. The head loss in the bend is 3 ft of water and the pressure at the inlet to the bend is 20 psi.

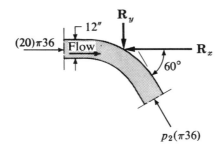

FIGURE 11-5

Solution: Figure 11-5 is a free-body diagram of the water in the bend. First, it is necessary to determine the pressure at the outlet to the bend by use of the Bernoulli equation. Thus,

$$\frac{20}{0.433} + 0 + \frac{v_1^2}{64.4} = \frac{p_2}{0.433} + 0 + \frac{v_2^2}{64.4} + 3.$$

Since the size of the pipe bend does not change, $v_1 = v_2$. Therefore,

$$\frac{p_2}{0.433} = \frac{20}{0.433} - 3 = 46.2 - 3 = 43.2 \text{ ft}$$

and

$$p_2 = 43.2(0.433) = 18.7 \text{ psi}.$$

Also,

$$v = \frac{Q}{a} = \frac{7.85}{0.785} = 10 \text{ fps.}$$

Now, applying the equation of impulse and momentum to the free-body diagram of Fig. 11-5, with the positive direction to the right, gives,

$$-\mathbf{R}_x + 20(36\pi) - 0.5(18.7)36\pi = 7.85(1.94)[0.5(10) - 10]$$

$$-\mathbf{R}_x + 2260 - 1055 = 15.24(-5) = -76.1$$

and

$$\mathbf{R}_x = 1281 \text{ lb} \leftarrow.$$

Therefore, the x component of the resultant pressure of the water on the bend is 1281 lb →.

The component of the reaction of the bend on the water in the y direction is

$$\mathbf{R}_y - 0.866(18.7)36\pi = 7.85(1.94)[0.866(10) - 0] = 132 \text{ lb.}$$

$$\mathbf{R}_y = 1964 \text{ lb} \downarrow$$

Therefore, the y component of the resultant pressure of the water on the bend is 1964 lb ↑.

Example 11-7. A 24-in.-diameter horizontal pipe line transmitting oil ($S_g = 0.80$) at 8 cfs, changes direction through a 30° horizontal reducing bend and discharges into an 18-in.-diameter pipe line. The head loss in the

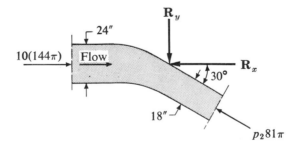

FIGURE 11-6

24-in. by 18-in. bend is 6 ft of oil. If the pressure at the inlet to the bend is 10 psi, determine the rectangular components of the resultant reaction of the bend on the oil, with one component in the direction of the 24-in. pipe line.

Solution: Figure 11-6 is a free-body diagram of the oil deflected in the bend. First, it is necessary to determine the pressure at the outlet of the bend. In this situation, v_1 does not equal v_2 since the pipe diameters at the entrance and outlet of the bend are not the same. Therefore,

$$v_1 = \frac{8}{\pi 1} = 2.55 \text{ fps.}$$

and

$$v_2 = \frac{8(16)}{\pi 9} = 4.53 \text{ fps.}$$

Substituting values into the Bernoulli equation, gives

$$\frac{10}{0.433(0.8)} + 0 + \frac{2.55^2}{64.4} = \frac{p_2}{0.433(0.8)} + 0 + \frac{4.53^2}{64.4} + 6.0$$

$$28.9 + 0.1 = \frac{p_2}{0.346} + 0 + 0.3 + 6.0$$

and

$$p_2 = 22.7(0.346) = 7.85 \text{ psi.}$$

Now, using the equation of impulse and momentum, applied to the free-body diagram of Fig. 11-6,

$$-R_x + 10(144\pi) - 0.866(7.85)81\pi = 8(1.94)0.8[0.866(4.53) - 2.55]$$

and

$$R_x = 4524 - 1730 - 17.0 = 2777 \text{ lb} \leftarrow.$$

Also,

$$R_y = 0.5(7.85)81\pi = 8(1.94)0.8[0.5(4.53) - 0]$$

and

$$R_y = 12.4(2.27) + 999 = 28 + 999 = 1027 \text{ lb} \downarrow.$$

Example 11-8.   Determine the resultant longitudinal thrust on a straight horizontal reducer, in which the diameter changes from 12-in. to 6-in. in the direction of flow, when the pipe is carrying 3.14 cfs of water. The gage pressure in the 12-in. section is 4 psi and the friction loss is 6 ft of water.

Solution: Figure 11-7 is the free-body diagram of the water passing through the reducer. First, the velocities at the inlet and outlet of the reducer must be found.

$$v_1 = \frac{3.14(4)}{\pi} = 4 \text{ fps}$$

and

$$v_2 = \frac{3.14(16)}{\pi} = 16 \text{ fps.}$$

Substituting all known values into the Bernoulli equation, gives,

$$\frac{4}{0.433} + 0 + \frac{4^2}{64.4} = \frac{p_2}{0.433} + 0 + \frac{16^2}{64.4} + 6.0$$

$$\frac{p_2}{0.433} = 9.23 + 0.25 - 3.97 - 6.0 = -9.97 + 9.48 = -0.49 \text{ ft}$$

and

$$p_2 = -0.49(0.433) = -0.212 \text{ psi (a vacuum).}$$

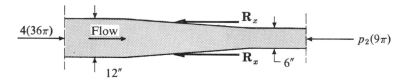

FIGURE 11-7

Now, applying the impulse and momentum equation to the free-body diagram of Fig. 11-7, with the positive direction to the right, gives

$$-R_x + 4(36\pi) - (-0.212)9\pi = 3.14(1.94)(16 - 4)$$

and

$$R_x = 452 + 5.94 - 73.09 = 384.9 \text{ lb} \leftarrow.$$

Therefore, the thrust of the water on the pipe is 384.9 lb →.

PROBLEMS

11-25. The diameter of a horizontal pipe carrying oil ($S_g = 0.85$) is reduced from 24-in. to 12-in. at a 60° bend in the line. The pressure in the 24-in. pipe is 4 psi when the discharge is 8 cfs. Determine the component of the reaction of the pipe on the oil in the direction parallel to the 24-in. section if the head loss in the reducer is 5 ft of oil.

11-26. The diameter of a horizontal pipe changes from 6-in. to 2-in. in the direction of flow at a 150° bend. The pipe carries 0.785 cfs of oil ($S_g = 0.85$) and the pressure at the entrance to the bend is 10 psi. If the component of the force, exerted by the oil on the bend parallel to the 6-in. pipe, is 320 lb in the direction of flow, determine the head loss in the reducing bend.

11-27. The diameter of a horizontal pipe, carrying acid ($\gamma = 75$ pcf) is reduced in the direction of flow from 6-in. to 2-in. at a 150° bend. If the velocity of the acid is 5 fps and the pressure is 10 psi at the inlet to the bend, determine the component of the force parallel to the 2-in. pipe exerted by the acid on the pipe. The lost head in the bend is 8 ft of acid.

11-28. The diameter of a horizontal pipe carrying muriatic acid ($S_g = 1.20$) is reduced in the direction of flow from 3-in. to 1-in. at a 150° bend. If the velocity of the acid is 5 fps and the pressure is 12 psi at the inlet to the bend, determine the magnitude of the component of the force that is exerted by the acid on the pipe. The force is parallel to the 1-in. pipe. The head loss in the bend is 6 ft of acid.

11-29. The diameter of a pipe at a 120° reducing bend in a horizontal plane is reduced in the direction of flow from 4-in. to 2-in. The pressure at the 4-in. section is 12 psi, the discharge is 1 cfs of water, and the head loss in the reducer is 7 ft of water. Determine the magnitude and sense of the component of the force exerted by the water on the reducer in the direction of the 4-in. pipe.

11-30. Water, under a pressure of 10 psi, flows with a velocity of 10 fps through a 60° horizontal bend having a uniform diameter of 12 in. Neglect the pressure drop in the bend. Determine the magnitude of the resultant fluid force on the bend.

11-31. The diameter of a horizontal pipe changes from 6 in. to 3 in. in the direction of flow at a 30° bend. The pipe carries 0.785 cfs of oil ($S_g = 0.85$) and the pressure at the 6-in. section is 12 psi. If the head loss in the reducing bend is 4 ft of oil, determine the component of the force exerted by the oil on the bend parallel to the 3-in. pipe.

11-32. The diameter of a horizontal pipe changes from 6-in. to 2-in. in the direction of flow at a 120° bend. The pipe carries 0.90 cfs of oil ($S_g = 0.87$) and the pressure at the 6-in. section is 12 psi. If the component of the force exerted by the oil on the bend parallel to the 6-in. pipe is 370 lb in the direction of flow, determine the head loss in the reducing bend.

11-33. The diameter of a horizontal pipe carrying oil ($S_g = 0.80$) is reduced in the direction of flow from 6-in. to 2-in. at a 120° bend. If the velocity of the oil is 3 fps and the pressure is 12 psi at the entrance to the bend, determine the component of the force that is exerted by the oil on the pipe. The force is parallel to the 6-in. pipe. The lost head in the bend is 6 ft of oil.

11-34. The diameter of a horizontal, 90° elbow is gradually reduced in the direction of flow from 2.0 ft to 1.0 ft. The pressure and velocity at the larger section are 5.0 psi and 5.0 fps, respectively. The head loss due to friction is 15 ft of water. Determine the component of the force exerted by the water on the elbow in the direction parallel to the exit velocity.

11-35. The diameter of a horizontal pipe changes from 9-in. to 3-in. in the direction of flow at a 60° reducing bend. The pipe carries 0.393 cfs of oil ($S_g = 0.80$) and the pressure at the inlet to the bend is 30 psi. If the head loss in the bend is 8 ft of oil, determine the component of the force exerted by the oil on the bend. The force is parallel to the 3-in. pipe.

11-36. The diameter of a horizontal pipe carrying oil ($S_g = 0.80$) is reduced in the direction of flow from 6-in. to 4-in. at a 120 degree bend. The velocity of the oil is 8 fps and the pressure is 20 psi at the 6-in. section. Determine the component of the force exerted by the pipe on the oil. The force is parallel to the 6-in. section. The head loss in the bend is 3 ft of oil.

Chapter 12

Dimensional Analysis
and Similitude

12-1 INTRODUCTION

In the process of setting up equations as bases for experimental analysis, it is important that every term of the equation be dimensionally compatible, that is, dimensionally correct. Forces may only be added to or equated to other forces, and stresses may only be added to or equated to other stresses. That is, each side of an equation must have the same units or dimensions to be dimensionally correct.

12-2 SYSTEMS OF DIMENSIONS

Currently, two systems of dimensions are in use in engineering: the force-length-time (*FLT*), and the mass-length-time (*MLT*) systems. In some areas, temperature is an added dimension.

Although dimensional analysis is useful in checking the consistency of equations, its principal use is in the formulation of equations for experimental work and in the design of models. Dimensional analysis permits the reduction of the variables pertinent to a situation requiring experimental analysis and simplifies the equation finally used in the analysis.

12-3 THE BUCKINGHAM Π THEOREM

The Buckingham Π theorem is a method used to reduce the number of variables in a problem that is to be investigated. If there are N variables to be considered and they may be expressed in terms of K dimensions, such as F, L, or T, then the variables may be reduced to N minus K Π terms. The Π terms, in turn, are dimensionless and are made up of combinations of the original variables.

For example, apply the Buckingham Π theorem to a circular plate, with a diameter, d, submerged in a liquid under a static condition. The magnitude of the force exerted on the plane of the circular plate may be expressed in terms of the specific weight, γ, the vertical distance from the surface of the liquid to the centroid of the plate, $\bar{h}$, the diameter of the plate, d, and the angle that the plate makes with the horizontal, θ. That is,

$$\mathbf{F} = f(\gamma, \bar{h}, d, \theta).$$

Using an analytical approach, and referring to the free-body diagram in Fig. 12-1, by $\sum \mathbf{F}_y = 0$,

$$W - P \cos \theta = 0, \quad \text{and} \quad W = P \cos \theta.$$

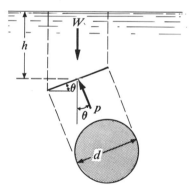

FIGURE 12-1

Since the fluid is static, no shear is exerted on the plate by the fluid, so that P acts normal to the inclined plate. Also,

$$W = \gamma(\text{volume of fluid}) = \gamma \bar{h} \frac{\pi d^2}{4} \cos \theta.$$

Therefore,

$$P = \gamma \bar{h} \frac{\pi d^2}{4}.$$

From the above, it appears that the magnitude of the force is independent of the inclination of the plane of the plate.

Now using the experimental approach, the variables in this problem and their dimensions are listed as follows:

P = force		F
γ = specific weight		FL^{-3}
$\bar{h}$ = centroidal distance		L
d = diameter of plate		L
θ = inclined angle in radians		dimensionless

There are five variables and two dimensions, F and L. Therefore, by the Buckingham Π theorem there are 5 minus 2, or 3 Π terms. Thus,

$$\Pi_1 = \phi(\Pi_2, \Pi_3).$$

Thus, the independent variables have been reduced from four to two. Since θ is already dimensionless, it will serve as one Π term without modification.

12-4 DETERMINATION OF Π TERMS

The Π terms must be dimensionless and independent. Although it may be possible to write a number of equations that include the proper number of Π terms, it is desirable to set up a relatively simple set. To determine the Π terms for the variables in the preceding article, the general equation is written in the form,

$$f(P^{C_1}, \gamma^{C_2}, \bar{h}^{C_3}, d^{C_4}, \theta^{C_5}) = \text{a constant.}$$

The dimensional equation is,

$$F^{C_1}, (FL^{-3})^{C_2}, L^{C_3}, L^{C_4} = F^0 L^0$$

For this equation to be dimensionally correct, the sum of the exponents of F and L must equal zero. Therefore, the two following algebraic equations may be written,

for F, $\qquad\qquad C_1 + C_2 = 0$

and

for L, $$-3C_2 + C_3 + C_4 = 0$$

These two equations have four unknowns. In order to solve, two values must be assigned. These may be assigned arbitrarily, provided the resulting equations become independent. For this example, values of C_1 and C_4 are assigned.

Assume $C_1 = 1$ Assume $C_1 = 0$
  and $C_4 = 0$.   and $C_4 = 1$.
  Then $C_2 = -1$ Then $C_2 = 0$
  and $C_3 = -3$.   and $C_3 = -1$.

Therefore,

$$\Pi_1 = \frac{P}{\gamma \bar{h}^3} \qquad\qquad \Pi_2 = \frac{d}{\bar{h}}$$

Thus,

$$\frac{P}{\gamma \bar{h}^3} = \Phi(d/\bar{h},\ \theta). \tag{12-1}$$

Equation (12-1) is one possible form of the equation. Each term in the equation is dimensionless. It may be used experimentally to determine the force P on a submerged plane surface, since only two independent variables, $d/\bar{h}$ and θ, need to be studied instead of the four variables, γ, $\bar{h}$, d and θ. Thus, by use of the Π theorem the experimental work is greatly reduced.

If $P/(\gamma \bar{h}^3)$ vs $d/\bar{h}$ is plotted for various values of θ, it will be found that the changes in θ do not affect the $P/(\gamma \bar{h}^3)$ vs $d/\bar{h}$ curves; they remain the same for all values of θ. This corroborates the results obtained by the analytical solution in Sec. 12-3. That is, the magnitude of the force, P, does not depend on the inclination of the plate with the horizontal.

12-5 II TERMS

There are three types of variables generally included in fluid problems:

1. Geometrical variables, such as length, width, or depth.
2. Properties of fluids, such as density or specific weight, viscosity, and surface tension.
3. Forces acting, such as a resultant force, pressure, and gravity.

Often the Π terms can be set up by visual inspection; care must be taken to make each term dimensionless. Certain characteristic combinations of variables to form Π terms have been developed by various investigators. These include,

(a) The Reynolds number, $R = (\rho v d)/\mu$, which represents the ratio of the inertia force of an element to the viscous force.

(b) The Froude number, $F = v/(gd)^{1/2}$, which represents the ratio of the inertia force to the gravitational force.

(c) The Weber number, $W = (\rho v^2 d)/\sigma$, which represents the ratio of the inertia force to the surface tension.

12-6 MODEL THEORY

Since the Π term is a dimensionless ratio describing an aspect of a physical system, the scale of the system does not alter the ratio. Thus, measurements can be made on a model of the system that is of a more convenient size rather than on the full scale prototype. That is, if two different sized versions of the same physical system are made, and the independent Π terms have the same numerical values, then the dependent Π terms will have the same numerical values. That is, if

$$\Pi_1 = \phi(\Pi_2 \ldots \Pi_{N-K})$$

for the prototype, and,

$$\Pi_1 = \phi(\Pi_2 \ldots \Pi_{N-K})$$

for the model, and, if the independent variables $\Pi_2 \ldots \Pi_{N-K}$ for both model and prototype have the same numerical values, then

$$\Pi_1 \text{ (of the prototype)} = \Pi_1 \text{ (of the model)}.$$

For example, assume that a model of a 100 ft pipe line, 10 in. in diameter and having a velocity of 2 ft/sec, is to be designed at one-tenth the size of the prototype in order to determine the pressure drop in the 100 ft prototype. First, the pertinent variables in the problem are listed as

p = pressure drop	FL^{-2}
L = length of pipe	L
d = diameter of pipe	L
v = velocity of water	LT^{-1}
ρ = density of the water	$(FT^2)/L^4$
μ = viscosity of the water	$(FT)/L^2$

The number of Π terms is $N - K$, or $6 - 3$, or 3 Π terms. Therefore,

$$\Pi_1 = f(\Pi_2, \Pi_3)$$

and the general equation may be written,

$$f(p^{C_1}, L^{C_2}, d^{C_3}, v^{C_4}, \rho^{C_5}, \mu^{C_6}) = \text{a constant}$$

and,

$$(FL^{-2})^{C_1}, L^{C_2}, L^{C_3}, (LT^{-1})^{C_4}, (FT^2L^{-4})^{C_5}, (FTL^{-2})^{C_6} = F^0 L^0 T^0.$$

Therefore,

for F $C_1 + C_5 + C_6 = 0$

for L $-2C_1 + C_2 + C_3 + C_4 - 4C_5 - 2C_6 = 0$

for T $-C_4 + 2C_5 + C_6 = 0.$

Since there are six variables and only three equations, three values must be assigned.

Assume $C_1 = 1$ Assume $C_1 = 0$
$C_3 = 0$ $C_2 = 1$
and $C_6 = 0.$ and $C_6 = 1.$
Then $C_5 = -1$ Then $C_5 = -1$
$C_4 = -2$ $C_4 = -1$
and $C_2 = 0,$ and $C_3 = -2,$

for which the Π terms are:

$$\frac{p}{\rho v^2} \quad \text{and} \quad \frac{\mu L}{\rho v d^2}$$

The second Π term can be separated into two Π terms, $\mu/(\rho v d)$, which is the Reynolds number, and L/d. Therefore, the Π terms may be expressed as

$$\frac{p}{\rho v^2} = \left(\frac{\mu}{\rho v d}, \frac{L}{d}\right)$$

Since this is a general equation and is applicable to both model and prototype, the design equations are,

$$\frac{L_m}{d_m} = \frac{L}{d}. \tag{12-2}$$

The length scale, n, is the length of the prototype divided by the length of the model (which in this case is 10). Therefore,

$$L = nL_m.$$

Substituting into Eq. (12-2), gives,

$$d_m = \frac{d}{n},$$

and

$$d = ndm.$$

Also,

$$\frac{\rho_m v_m d_m}{\mu_m} = \frac{\rho v d}{\mu}.$$

Substituting the scale length into this equation, gives

$$\frac{\rho_m v_m}{\mu_m} = \frac{\rho v n}{\mu}.$$

Now, if the same fluid is used in the model as in the prototype, that is,

$$\frac{\rho_m}{\mu_m} = \frac{\rho}{\mu}$$

then

$$v_m = nv = 10v.$$

That is, the velocity in the model must be ten times the velocity in the prototype. These equations represent the design conditions. Now, equating the dependent Π terms, $\Pi_{1m} = \Pi_1$

$$\frac{p_m}{\rho_m v_m^2} = \frac{p}{\rho v^2}$$

Since $\rho_m = \rho$, and $v_m = 10v$,

$$p = \frac{p_m}{10^2},$$

which is the prediction equation. If it is assumed that the pressure drop in the 10-ft model, as measured, is 10 psi, the pressure drop in the 100 ft prototype is calculated to be

$$p = \frac{10}{10^2} = 0.10 \text{ psi}.$$

Appendix A

COMMERCIAL WROUGHT STEEL PIPE DATA*
(Per ASA B36.10-1950)

Nominal Pipe Size inches	Outside Diameter inches	Thickness inches	Inside Diameter inches (d)	Inside Diameter feet (D)	Inside Diameter Functions inches (d²)	(d³)	(d⁴)	(d⁵)	Transverse Internal Area sq in. (a)	sq ft (A)
					Standard Wall Pipe					
⅛	0.405	0.068	0.269	0.0224	0.0724	0.0195	0.00524	0.00141	0.057	0.00040
¼	0.540	0.088	0.364	0.0303	0.1325	0.0482	0.01756	0.00639	0.104	0.00072
⅜	0.675	0.091	0.493	0.0411	0.2430	0.1198	0.05905	0.02912	0.191	0.00133
½	0.840	0.109	0.622	0.0518	0.3869	0.2406	0.1497	0.0931	0.304	0.00211
¾	1.050	0.113	0.824	0.0687	0.679	0.5595	0.4610	0.3799	0.533	0.00371
1	1.315	0.133	1.049	0.0874	1.100	1.154	1.210	1.270	0.864	0.00600
1¼	1.660	0.140	1.380	0.1150	1.904	2.628	3.625	5.005	1.495	0.01040
1½	1.900	0.145	1.610	0.1342	2.592	4.173	6.718	10.82	2.036	0.01414
2	2.375	0.154	2.067	0.1722	4.272	8.831	18.250	37.72	3.355	0.02330
2½	2.875	0.203	2.469	0.2057	6.096	15.051	37.161	91.75	4.788	0.03322
3	3.500	0.216	3.068	0.2557	9.413	28.878	88.605	271.8	7.393	0.05130
3½	4.000	0.226	3.548	0.2957	12.59	44.663	158.51	562.2	9.886	0.06870
4	4.500	0.237	4.026	0.3355	16.21	65.256	262.76	1058.0	12.730	0.08840
5	5.563	0.258	5.047	0.4206	25.47	128.56	648.72	3275.0	20.006	0.1390
6	6.625	0.280	6.065	0.5054	36.78	223.10	1352.8	8206.0	28.891	0.2006
8	8.625	0.277	8.071	0.6725	65.14	525.75	4243.0	34248.0	51.161	0.3553
	8.625S	0.322	7.981	0.6651	63.70	508.36	4057.7	32380.0	50.027	0.3474
10	10.75	0.279	10.192	0.8493	103.88	1058.7	10789.0	109876.0	81.585	0.5666
	10.75	0.307	10.136	0.8446	102.74	1041.4	10555.0	106987.0	80.691	0.5604
	10.75S	0.365	10.020	0.8350	100.4	1006.0	10080.0	101000.0	78.855	0.5475
12	12.75	0.330	12.090	1.0075	146.17	1767.2	21366.0	258300.0	114.80	0.7972
	12.75S	0.375	12.000	1.000	144.0	1728.0	20736.0	248800.0	113.10	0.7854

COMMERCIAL WROUGHT STEEL PIPE DATA* (cont.)

Nominal Pipe Size inches	Outside Diameter inches	Thickness inches	Inside Diameter inches (d)	Inside Diameter feet (D)	Inside Diameter Functions inches (d^2)	(d^3)	(d^4)	(d^5)	Transverse Internal Area sq in. (a)	sq ft (A)
					Extra Strong Pipe					
⅛	0.405	0.095	0.215	0.0179	0.0462	0.00994	0.002134	0.000459	0.036	0.00025
¼	0.540	0.119	0.302	0.0252	0.0912	0.0275	0.008317	0.002513	0.072	0.00050
⅜	0.675	0.126	0.423	0.0353	0.1789	0.0757	0.03201	0.01354	0.141	0.00098
½	0.840	0.147	0.546	0.0455	0.2981	0.1628	0.08886	0.04852	0.234	0.00163
¾	1.050	0.154	0.742	0.0618	0.5506	0.4085	0.3032	0.2249	0.433	0.00300
1	1.315	0.179	0.957	0.0797	0.9158	0.8765	0.8387	0.8027	0.719	0.00499
1¼	1.660	0.191	1.278	0.1065	1.633	2.087	2.6667	3.409	1.283	0.00891
1½	1.900	0.200	1.500	0.1250	2.250	3.375	5.062	7.594	1.767	0.01225
2	2.375	0.218	1.939	0.1616	3.760	7.290	14.136	27.41	2.953	0.02050
2½	2.875	0.276	2.323	0.1936	5.396	12.536	29.117	67.64	4.238	0.02942
3	3.500	0.300	2.900	0.2417	8.410	24.389	70.728	205.1	6.605	0.04587
3½	4.000	0.318	3.364	0.2803	11.32	38.069	128.14	430.8	8.888	0.06170
4	4.500	0.337	3.826	0.3188	14.64	56.006	214.33	819.8	11.497	0.07986
5	5.563	0.375	4.813	0.4011	23.16	111.49	536.6	2583.0	18.194	0.1263
6	6.625	0.432	5.761	0.4801	33.19	191.20	1101.6	6346.0	26.067	0.1810
8	8.625	0.500	7.625	0.6354	58.14	443.32	3380.3	25775.0	45.663	0.3171
10	10.75	0.500	9.750	0.8125	95.06	926.86	9036.4	88110.0	74.662	0.5185
12	12.75	0.500	11.750	0.9792	138.1	1622.2	19072.0	223970.0	108.434	0.7528

Double Extra Strong Pipe

½	0.840	0.294	0.252	0.0210	0.0635	0.0160	0.004032	0.00102	0.050	0.00035
¾	1.050	0.308	0.434	0.0362	0.1884	0.0817	0.03549	0.01540	0.148	0.00103
1	1.315	0.358	0.599	0.0499	0.3588	0.2149	0.1287	0.07711	0.282	0.00196
1¼	1.660	0.382	0.896	0.0747	0.8028	0.7193	0.6445	0.5775	0.630	0.00438
1½	1.900	0.400	1.100	0.0917	1.210	1.331	1.4641	1.611	0.950	0.00660
2	2.375	0.436	1.503	0.1252	2.259	3.395	5.1031	7.670	1.774	0.01232
2½	2.875	0.552	1.771	0.1476	3.136	5.554	9.8345	17.42	2.464	0.01710
3	3.500	0.600	2.300	0.1917	5.290	12.167	27.984	64.36	4.155	0.02885
3½	4.000	0.636	2.728	0.2273	7.442	20.302	55.383	151.1	5.845	0.04059
4	4.500	0.674	3.152	0.2627	9.935	31.315	98.704	311.1	7.803	0.05419
5	5.563	0.750	4.063	0.3386	16.51	67.072	272.58	1107.0	12.966	0.09006
6	6.625	0.864	4.897	0.4081	23.98	117.43	575.04	2816.0	18.835	0.1308
8	8.625	0.875	6.875	0.5729	47.27	324.95	2234.4	15360.0	37.122	0.2578

* Reproduced from Technical Paper #410, *Flow of Fluids*, Courtesy of Crane Co.

COMMERCIAL WROUGHT STEEL PIPE DATA*
Schedule Wall Thickness—Per ASA B36.10-1950

Nominal Pipe Size inches	Outside Diameter inches	Thickness inches	Inside Diameter inches (d)	Inside Diameter feet (D)	Inside Diameter Functions inches (d^2)	(d^3)	(d^4)	(d^5)	Transverse Internal Area sq in. (a)	sq ft (A)
Schedule 10										
14	14	0.250	13.5	1.125	182.25	2460.4	33215.0	448400.0	143.14	0.994
16	16	0.250	15.5	1.291	240.25	3723.9	57720.0	894660.0	188.69	1.310
18	18	0.250	17.5	1.4583	306.25	5359.4	93789.0	1641309.0	240.53	1.670
20	20	0.250	19.5	1.625	380.25	7414.9	144590.0	2819500.0	298.65	2.074
24	24	0.250	23.5	1.958	552.25	12977.0	304980.0	7167030.0	433.74	3.012
30	30	0.312	29.376	2.448	862.95	25350.0	744288.0	21864218.0	677.76	4.707
Schedule 20										
8	8.625	0.250	8.125	0.6771	66.02	536.38	4359.3	35409.0	51.85	0.3601
10	10.75	0.250	10.25	0.8542	105.06	1076.9	11038.0	113141.0	82.52	0.5731
12	12.75	0.250	12.25	1.021	150.06	1838.3	22518.0	275855.0	117.86	0.8185
14	14.00	0.312	13.376	1.111	178.92	2393.2	32012.0	428185.0	140.52	0.9758
16	16	0.312	15.376	1.281	236.42	3635.2	55894.0	859442.0	185.69	1.290
18	18	0.312	17.376	1.448	301.92	5246.3	91156.0	1583978.0	237.13	1.647
20	20	0.375	19.250	1.604	370.56	7133.3	137317.0	2643352.0	291.04	2.021
24	24	0.375	23.25	1.937	540.56	12568.0	292205.0	6793832.0	424.56	2.948
30	30	0.500	29.00	2.417	841.00	24389.0	707281.0	20511149.0	660.52	4.587
Schedule 30										
8	8.625	0.277	8.071	0.6726	65.14	525.75	4243.2	34248.0	51.16	0.3553
10	10.75	0.307	10.136	0.8447	102.74	1041.4	10555.0	106987.0	80.69	0.5603
12	12.75	0.330	12.09	1.0075	146.17	1767.2	21366.0	258304.0	114.80	0.7972
14	14.00	0.375	13.25	1.1042	175.56	2326.2	30824.0	408394.0	137.88	0.9575
16	16	0.375	15.25	1.2708	232.56	3546.6	54084.0	824801.0	182.65	1.268
18	18	0.438	17.124	1.4270	293.23	5021.3	85984.0	1472397.0	230.30	1.599
20	20	0.500	19.00	1.5833	361.00	6859.0	130321.0	2476099.0	283.53	1.969
24	24	0.562	22.876	1.9063	523.31	11971.0	273853.0	6264703.0	411.00	2.854
30	30	0.625	28.75	2.3958	826.56	23764.0	683201.0	19642160.0	649.18	4.508

Schedule 40

Size										
1/8	0.405	0.068	0.269	0.0224	0.0724	0.0195	0.005242	0.00141	0.057	0.00040
1/4	0.540	0.088	0.364	0.0303	0.1325	0.0482	0.01756	0.00639	0.104	0.00072
3/8	0.675	0.091	0.493	0.0411	0.2430	0.1198	0.05905	0.02912	0.191	0.00133
1/2	0.840	0.109	0.622	0.0518	0.3869	0.2406	0.1497	0.09310	0.304	0.00211
3/4	1.050	0.113	0.824	0.0687	0.679	0.5595	0.4610	0.3799	0.533	0.00371
1	1.315	0.133	1.049	0.0874	1.100	1.154	1.210	1.270	0.864	0.00600
1 1/4	1.660	0.140	1.380	0.1150	1.904	2.628	3.625	5.005	1.495	0.01040
1 1/2	1.900	0.145	1.610	0.1342	2.592	4.173	6.718	10.82	2.036	0.01414
2	2.375	0.154	2.067	0.1722	4.272	8.831	18.250	37.72	3.355	0.02330
2 1/2	2.875	0.203	2.469	0.2057	6.096	15.051	37.161	91.75	4.788	0.03322
3	3.500	0.216	3.068	0.2557	9.413	28.878	88.605	271.8	7.393	0.05130
3 1/2	4.000	0.226	3.548	0.2957	12.59	44.663	158.51	562.2	9.886	0.06870
4	4.500	0.237	4.026	0.3355	16.21	65.256	262.76	1058.0	12.730	0.08840
5	5.563	0.258	5.047	0.4206	25.47	128.56	648.72	3275.0	20.006	0.1390
6	6.625	0.280	6.065	0.5054	36.78	223.10	1352.8	8206.0	28.891	0.2006
8	8.625	0.322	7.981	0.6651	63.70	508.36	4057.7	32380.0	50.027	0.3474
10	10.75	0.365	10.02	0.8350	100.40	1006.0	10080.0	101000.0	78.855	0.5475
12	12.75	0.406	11.938	0.9965	142.50	1701.3	20306.0	242470.0	111.93	0.7773
14	14.00	0.438	13.124	1.0937	172.24	2260.5	29666.0	389340.0	135.28	0.9394
16	16.0	0.500	15.000	1.250	225.0	3375.0	50625.0	759375.0	176.72	1.2272
18	18.0	0.562	16.876	1.4063	284.8	4806.3	81111.0	1368820.0	223.68	1.5533
20	20.0	0.593	18.814	1.5678	354.0	6659.5	125320.0	2357244.0	278.00	1.9305
24	24.0	0.687	22.626	1.8855	511.9	11583.0	262040.0	5929784.0	402.07	2.7921

Schedule 60

Size										
8	8.625	0.406	7.813	0.6511	61.04	476.93	3725.9	29113.0	47.94	0.3329
10	10.75	0.500	9.750	0.8125	95.06	926.86	9036.4	88110.0	74.66	0.5185
12	12.75	0.562	11.626	0.9688	135.16	1571.4	18268.0	212399.0	106.16	0.7372
14	14.00	0.593	12.814	1.0678	164.20	2104.0	26962.0	345480.0	128.96	0.8956
16	16.0	0.656	14.688	1.2240	215.74	3168.8	46544.0	683618.0	169.44	1.1766
18	18.0	0.750	16.500	1.3750	272.25	4492.1	74120.0	1222982.0	213.83	1.4849
20	20.0	0.812	18.376	1.5313	337.68	6205.2	114028.0	2095342.0	265.21	1.8417
24	24.0	0.968	22.064	1.8387	486.82	10741.0	236994.0	5229036.0	382.35	2.6552

COMMERCIAL WROUGHT STEEL PIPE DATA* (cont.)

Nominal Pipe Size	Outside Diameter	Thick-ness	Inside Diameter		Inside Diameter Functions inches				Transverse Internal Area	
inches	inches	inches	inches (d)	feet (D)	(d²)	(d³)	(d⁴)	(d⁵)	sq in. (a)	sq ft (A)
1/8	0.405	0.095	0.215	0.0179	0.0462	0.00994	0.002134	0.000459	0.036	0.00025
1/4	0.540	0.119	0.302	0.0252	0.0912	0.0275	0.008317	0.002513	0.072	0.00050
3/8	0.675	0.126	0.423	0.0353	0.1789	0.0757	0.03200	0.01354	0.141	0.00098
1/2	0.840	0.147	0.546	0.0455	0.2981	0.1628	0.08886	0.04852	0.234	0.00163
3/4	1.050	0.154	0.742	0.0618	0.5506	0.4085	0.3032	0.2249	0.433	0.00300
1	1.315	0.179	0.957	0.0797	0.9158	0.8765	0.8387	0.8027	0.719	0.00499
1 1/4	1.660	0.191	1.278	0.1065	1.633	2.087	2.6667	3.409	1.283	0.00891
1 1/2	1.900	0.200	1.500	0.1250	2.250	3.375	5.062	7.594	1.767	0.01225
2	2.375	0.218	1.939	0.1616	3.760	7.290	14.136	27.41	2.953	0.02050
2 1/2	2.875	0.276	2.323	0.1936	5.396	12.536	29.117	67.64	4.238	0.02942
3	3.5	0.300	2.900	0.2417	8.410	24.389	70.728	205.1	6.605	0.04587
3 1/2	4.0	0.318	3.364	0.2803	11.32	38.069	128.14	430.8	8.888	0.06170
4	4.5	0.337	3.826	0.3188	14.64	56.006	214.33	819.8	11.497	0.07986
5	5.563	0.375	4.813	0.4011	23.16	111.49	536.38	2583.0	18.194	0.1263
6	6.625	0.432	5.761	0.4801	33.19	191.20	1101.6	6346.0	26.067	0.1810
8	8.625	0.500	7.625	0.6354	58.14	443.32	3380.3	25775.0	45.663	0.3171
10	10.75	0.593	9.564	0.7970	91.47	874.82	8366.8	80020.0	71.84	0.4989
12	12.75	0.687	11.376	0.9480	129.41	1472.2	16747.0	190523.0	101.64	0.7058
14	14.0	0.750	12.500	1.0417	156.25	1953.1	24414.0	305176.0	122.72	0.8522
16	16.0	0.843	14.314	1.1928	204.89	2932.8	41980.0	600904.0	160.92	1.1175
18	18.0	0.937	16.126	1.3488	260.05	4193.5	67626.0	1090518.0	204.24	1.4183
20	20.0	1.031	17.938	1.4948	321.77	5771.9	103536.0	1857248.0	252.72	1.7550
24	24.0	1.218	21.564	1.7970	465.01	10027.0	216234.0	4662798.0	365.22	2.5362

Schedule 80

Schedule 100

8	8.625	0.593	7.439	0.6199	55.34	411.66	3062.0	22781.0	43.46	0.3018
10	10.75	0.718	9.314	0.7762	86.75	807.99	7526.0	69357.0	68.13	0.4732
12	12.25	0.843	11.064	0.9220	122.41	1354.4	14985.0	165791.0	96.14	0.6677
14	14.0	0.937	12.126	1.0105	147.04	1783.0	21621.0	262173.0	115.49	0.8020
16	16.0	1.031	13.938	1.1615	194.27	2707.7	37740.0	526020.0	152.58	1.0596
18	18.0	1.156	15.688	1.3057	246.11	3861.0	60572.0	950250.0	193.30	1.3423
20	20.0	1.281	17.438	1.4532	304.08	5302.6	92467.0	1612438.0	238.83	1.6585
24	24.0	1.531	20.938	1.7448	438.40	9179.2	192195.0	4024179.0	344.32	2.3911

Schedule 120

4	4.50	0.438	3.624	0.302	13.133	47.595	172.49	625.1	10.315	0.07163
5	5.563	0.500	4.563	0.3802	20.82	95.006	433.5	1978.0	16.35	0.1136
6	6.625	0.562	5.501	0.4584	30.26	166.47	915.7	5037.0	23.77	0.1650
8	8.625	0.718	7.189	0.5991	51.68	371.54	2671.0	19202.0	40.59	0.2819
10	10.75	0.843	9.064	0.7553	82.16	744.66	6750.0	61179.0	64.53	0.4481
12	12.75	1.000	10.750	0.8959	115.56	1242.3	13355.0	143563.0	90.76	0.6303
14	14.0	1.093	11.814	0.9845	139.57	1648.9	19480.0	230137.0	109.62	0.7612
16	16.0	1.218	13.564	1.1303	183.98	2495.5	33849.0	459133.0	144.50	1.0035
18	18.0	1.375	15.250	1.2708	232.56	3546.6	54086.0	824804.0	182.66	1.2684
20	20.0	1.500	17.000	1.4166	289.00	4913.0	83521.0	1419857.0	226.98	1.5762
24	24.0	1.812	20.376	1.6980	415.18	8459.7	172375.0	3512313.0	326.08	2.2645

Schedule 140

8	8.625	0.812	7.001	0.5834	49.01	343.15	2402.0	16819.0	38.50	0.2673
10	10.75	1.000	8.750	0.7292	76.56	669.92	5862.0	51291.0	60.13	0.4176
12	12.75	1.125	10.500	0.8750	110.25	1157.6	12155.0	127628.0	86.59	0.6013
14	14.0	1.250	11.500	0.9583	132.25	1520.9	17490.0	201136.0	103.87	0.7213
16	16.0	1.438	13.124	1.0937	172.24	2260.5	29666.0	389340.0	135.28	0.9394
18	18.0	1.562	14.876	1.2396	221.30	3292.0	48972.0	728502.0	173.80	1.2070
20	20.0	1.750	16.5	1.3750	272.25	4492.1	74120.0	1222981.0	213.82	1.4849
24	24.0	2.062	19.876	1.6563	395.06	7852.1	156069.0	3102022.0	310.28	2.1547

* Reproduced from Technical Paper #410, *Flow of Fluids*, Courtesy of Crane Co.

COMMERCIAL WROUGHT STEEL PIPE DATA*

Nominal Pipe Size inches	Outside Diameter inches	Thickness inches	Inside Diameter inches (d)	Inside Diameter feet (D)	(d^2)	(d^3)	(d^4)	(d^5)	Transverse Internal Area sq in. (a)	Transverse Internal Area sq ft (A)
½	0.840	0.187	0.466	0.0388	0.2172	0.1012	0.04716	0.02197	0.1706	0.00118
¾	1.050	0.218	0.614	0.0512	0.3770	0.2315	0.1421	0.08726	0.2961	0.00206
1	1.315	0.250	0.815	0.0679	0.6642	0.5413	0.4412	0.3596	0.5217	0.00362
1¼	1.660	0.250	1.160	0.0966	1.346	1.561	1.811	2.100	1.057	0.00734
1½	1.900	0.281	1.338	0.1115	1.790	2.395	3.205	4.288	1.406	0.00976
2	2.375	0.343	1.689	0.1407	2.853	4.818	8.138	13.74	2.241	0.01556
2½	2.875	0.375	2.125	0.1771	4.516	9.596	20.39	43.33	3.546	0.02463
3	3.50	0.438	2.624	0.2187	6.885	18.067	47.41	124.4	5.408	0.03755
4	4.50	0.531	3.438	0.2865	11.82	40.637	139.7	480.3	9.283	0.06447
5	5.563	0.625	4.313	0.3594	18.60	80.230	346.0	1492.0	14.61	0.1015
6	6.625	0.718	5.189	0.4324	26.93	139.72	725.0	3762.0	21.15	0.1469
8	8.625	0.906	6.813	0.5677	46.42	316.24	2155.0	14679.0	36.46	0.2532
10	10.75	1.125	8.500	0.7083	72.25	614.12	5220.0	44371.0	56.75	0.3941
12	12.75	1.312	10.126	0.8438	102.54	1038.3	10514.0	106461.0	80.53	0.5592
14	14.0	1.406	11.188	0.9323	125.17	1400.4	15668.0	175292.0	98.31	0.6827
16	16.0	1.593	12.814	1.0678	164.20	2104.0	26961.0	345482.0	128.96	0.8956
18	18.0	1.781	14.438	1.2032	208.45	3009.7	43454.0	627387.0	163.72	1.1369
20	20.0	1.968	16.064	1.3387	258.05	4145.3	66590.0	1069715.0	202.67	1.4074
24	24.0	2.343	19.314	1.6095	373.03	7204.7	139152.0	2687582.0	292.98	2.0346

Schedule 160

* Reproduced from Technical Paper #410, *Flow of Fluids*, Courtesy of Crane Co.

234

Appendix B

STAINLESS STEEL PIPE DATA*
Schedule Wall Thickness—Per ASA B36.19-1957

Nominal Pipe Size	Outside Diameter	Thickness	Inside Diameter		Inside Diameter Functions inches				Transverse Internal Area	
inches	inches	inches	inches (d)	feet (D)	(d^2)	(d^3)	(d^4)	(d^5)	sq in. (a)	sq ft (A)
					Schedule 5 S					
½	0.840	0.065	0.710	0.0592	0.504	0.358	0.254	0.1804	0.396	0.00275
¾	1.050	0.065	0.920	0.0767	0.846	0.779	0.716	0.659	0.664	0.00461
1	1.315	0.065	1.185	0.0988	1.404	1.664	1.972	2.337	1.103	0.00766
1¼	1.660	0.065	1.530	0.1275	2.341	3.582	5.480	8.384	1.839	0.01277
1½	1.900	0.065	1.770	0.1475	3.133	5.545	9.815	17.37	2.461	0.01709
2	2.375	0.065	2.245	0.1871	5.040	11.31	25.40	57.03	3.958	0.02749
2½	2.875	0.083	2.709	0.2258	7.339	19.88	53.86	145.9	5.764	0.04003
3	3.500	0.083	3.334	0.2778	11.12	37.06	123.6	411.9	8.733	0.06065
3½	4.000	0.083	3.834	0.3195	14.70	56.36	216.1	828.4	11.545	0.08017
4	4.500	0.083	4.334	0.3612	18.78	81.41	352.8	1529.0	14.750	0.1024
5	5.563	0.109	5.345	0.4454	28.57	152.7	816.2	4363.0	22.439	0.1558
6	6.625	0.109	6.407	0.5339	41.05	263.0	1685.0	10796.0	32.241	0.2239
8	8.625	0.109	8.407	0.7006	70.68	594.2	4995.0	41996.0	55.512	0.3855
10	10.750	0.134	10.482	0.8375	109.9	1152.0	12072.0	126538.0	86.315	0.5994
12	12.750	0.156	12.438	1.0365	154.7	1924.0	23933.0	297682.0	121.50	0.8438

STAINLESS STEEL PIPE DATA*
Schedule Wall Thickness—Per ASA B36.19-1957

Nominal Pipe Size	Outside Diameter	Thickness	Inside Diameter		Inside Diameter Functions inches				Transverse Internal Area	
inches	inches	inches	inches (d)	feet (D)	(d^2)	(d^3)	(d^4)	(d^5)	sq ft (A)	sq in. (a)
					Schedule 10 S					
⅛	0.405	0.049	0.307	0.0256	0.0942	0.0289	0.00888	0.00273	0.074	0.00051
¼	0.540	0.065	0.410	0.0342	0.1681	0.0689	0.02826	0.01159	0.132	0.00092
⅜	0.675	0.065	0.545	0.0454	0.2970	0.1619	0.08822	0.04808	0.233	0.00162
½	0.840	0.083	0.674	0.0562	0.4543	0.3062	0.2064	0.1391	0.357	0.00248
¾	1.050	0.083	0.884	0.0737	0.7815	0.6908	0.6107	0.5398	0.614	0.00426
1	1.315	0.109	1.097	0.0914	1.203	1.320	1.448	1.589	0.945	0.00656
1¼	1.660	0.109	1.442	0.1202	2.079	2.998	4.324	6.235	1.633	0.01134
1½	1.900	0.109	1.682	0.1402	2.829	4.759	8.004	13.46	2.222	0.01543
2	2.375	0.109	2.157	0.1798	4.653	10.04	21.65	46.69	3.654	0.02538
2½	2.875	0.120	2.635	0.2196	6.943	18.30	48.21	127.0	5.453	0.03787
3	3.500	0.120	3.260	0.2717	10.63	34.65	112.9	368.2	8.347	0.05796
3½	4.000	0.120	3.760	0.3133	14.14	53.16	199.9	751.5	11.11	0.07712
4	4.500	0.120	4.260	0.3550	18.15	77.31	329.3	1403.0	14.26	0.09899
5	5.563	0.134	5.295	0.4413	28.04	148.5	786.1	4162.0	22.02	0.1529
6	6.625	0.134	6.357	0.5298	40.41	256.9	1633.0	10382.0	31.74	0.2204

8	8.625	0.148	8.329	0.6941	69.37	577.8	4813.0	40083.0	54.48	0.3784
10	10.750	0.165	10.420	0.8683	108.6	1131.0	11789.0	122840.0	85.29	0.5923
12	12.750	0.180	12.390	1.0325	153.5	1902.0	23566.0	291982.0	120.6	0.8372

Schedule 40 S

⅛ to 12	Values are the same for the various sizes as those given for Standard Wall Pipe (heaviest weight on 8, 10, and 12-inch sizes).

Schedule 80 S

⅛ to 12	Values are the same for the various sizes as those given for Extra Strong Pipe.

* Reproduced from Technical Paper #410, *Flow of Fluids*, Courtesy of Crane Co.

Answers to Even-Numbered Problems

CHAPTER 1

1-2.	(a) 56.35 pcf	**1-18.**	water at 4C
	(b) 0.903	**1-20.**	7.35 psig
1-4.	0.00594 lb	**1-22.**	26.02 psia
1-6.	0.0053 lb	**1-24.**	78.63 psia
1-8.	0.923 in.	**1-26.**	66.75 psig
1-10.	0.00166 psi	**1-28.**	0.000898 pcf lighter
1-12.	$458(10^{-6})$ ft-lb	**1-30.**	83,330 psi
1-14.	0.1564 stokes	**1-32.**	15.16 poises
1-16.	48.7 sec	**1-34.**	1235 in.-lb

CHAPTER 2

2-2.	3.28 psig	**2-14.**	11.9 psia
2-4.	39.8 ft	**2-16.**	6.90 ft
2-6.	22.2 in.	**2-18.**	17.5 in.
2-8.	1872 psf	**2-20.**	83.6 ft water
2-10.	1.25 ft	**2-22.**	6.01 in.
2-12.	11.97 psig	**2-24.**	13.05 in.

241

2-26. 2.25 psig
2-28. 0.84 ft
2-30. 784 ft-lb
2-32. 1.88 ft
2-34. 7071 lb
2-36. 6.93 ft
2-38. $A_x = 5763$ lb $\leftarrow$
$A_y = 29,349$ lb $\downarrow$
$B = 29,350$ lb $\rightarrow$

2-40. 10,039 lb $\downarrow$; $A_x = 6390$ lb;
$A_y = 0$ lb
2-42. 48,987 ft-lb
2-44. 0.15 in.
2-46. (a) 2.70
(b) 0.462
2-48. 53,916 ft-lb
2-50. 0.298

CHAPTER 3

3-2. 39.9 pcf
3-4. 1.841 slugs/cu ft
3-6. 166.4 pcf
3-8. 39.9 pcf; 150.3 lb

3-10. 374.4 lb $\downarrow$ thru centroid
3-12. 2.91 ft
3-14. 6.99 cu ft

CHAPTER 4

4-2. 3.40 fps
4-4. 1.547 cfs
4-6. (a) 83.14 ft of water
(b) 0.405 ft of water
(c) 93.55 ft of water
4-8. $A \rightarrow B$
14.12 ft of water
4-10. 15.54 psig
4-12. 3.74 psig
4-14. 31.41 psig
4-16. 2.23 cfs

4-18. 14.96 psig
4-20. 8.66 ft of water
4-22. (a) 0.99 ft-lb/lb
(b) 21.7 ft-lb/ft
4-24. 1.11 cfs
4-26. 81,680 hp
4-28. 34.7 psig
4-30. 21.66 hp
4-32. 69.9 percent
4-34. 184.5 ft
4-36. 62.4 hp

CHAPTER 5

5-2. 61.47
5-4. 22.83 fps
5-6. 69.48 fps
5-8. 1.80 fps
5-10. 23.37 ft kerosene.
5-12. 0.217 ft oil/ft
5-14. 29.33 hp
5-16. 37.79 psig

5-18. (a) 4241 hp
(b) 4394 hp
5-20. 2.10 ft water/1000 ft
5-22. 33.28 in.
5-24. 1.62 cfs
5-26. 4.42 cfs
5-28. 2.31 cfs
5-30. 1.21 cfs

5-32.	1.89 cfs	**5-48.**	25.50 psig
5-34.	10.17 cfs	**5-50.**	1.78 ft
5-36.	0.052 cfs	**5-52.**	0.056 ft water
5-38.	6.82 in.	**5-54.**	A 2.11 cfs
5-40.	6.17 in.		B 0.89 cfs
5-42.	919.6 hp	**5-56.**	a 2.34 cfs
5-44.	20.88 hp		b 1.66 cfs
5-46.	4.69 cfs		

CHAPTER 6

6-2.	11.86 in.	**6-30.**	0.580 cfs
6-4.	21.45 psig	**6-32.**	1.29 cfs
6-6.	42.91 cfs	**6-34.**	20.44 ft oil
6-8.	2.82 cfs	**6-36.**	14.03 ft oil
6-10.	6.17 cfs	**6-38.**	0.628
6-12.	1.59 cfs	**6-40.**	(a) 0.578
6-14.	0.937		(b) 0.623
6-16.	141.2 psig		(c) 0.361
6-18.	46.19 psig	**6-42.**	0.784
6-20.	(a) 64.55 psig	**6-44.**	26.27 in.
	(b) 28.32 ft water	**6-46.**	58.17 in.
6-22.	79.22 fps	**6-48.**	0.942 cfs
6-24.	84.54 psig	**6-50.**	2.51 ft
6-26.	0.503 cfs	**6-52.**	41.43 ft
6-28.	96.51 psig	**6-54.**	0.435 cfs

CHAPTER 7

7-2.	0.574 cfs	**7-10.**	9.58 psig
7-4.	0.359 ft water	**7-12.**	-13.72 psig
7-6.	$C_v = 0.941$	**7-14.**	29.92 ft water
	$C_c = 0.616$	**7-16.**	1.71 in.
7-8.	0.819		

CHAPTER 8

8-2.	4.94 ft	**8-8.**	7.49 ft
8-4.	1042 cfs	**8-10.**	$d = 5.56$ ft
8-6.	0.00045		$b = 11.12$ ft

8-12. 2.50 ft

8-14. 395.6 cfs

8-16. 0.000306

8-18. $d = 1.125$ ft
$b = 17.75$ ft

8-20. 1725 cfs

8-22. $b = d = 7.44$ ft

8-24. 3.58 ft

8-26. $d = 4.09$ ft
$b = 2.48$ ft

8-28. 0.000233

8-30. $d = 3.70$ ft
$b = 1.42$ ft

8-32. $d = 2.55$ ft

8-34. 0.255 ft

8-36. 0.185 ft

8-38. Subcritical

8-40. Supercritical
0.00179

8-42. 454 cfs

CHAPTER 9

9-2. 0.000026

9-4. 1.13 ft

9-6. 11.02 ft

9-8. 4.66 cfs

9-10. 0.963 ft

9-12. 22.69 cfs

9-14. 155.0 cfs

9-16. 0.441 ft

9-18. 10.53 ft

9-20. 2.14 ft

9-22. 4.44 cfs

9-24. 6 weirs

9-26. $d = 1.80$ ft
$b = 3.60$ ft
3.87 ft below water surface

9-28. 3 weirs

9-30. 2.55 ft

9-32. $d = 1.25$ ft
$b = 10.05$ ft

9-34. 10 weirs

9-36. (a) 3.29 ft
(b) $d = 1.97$ ft
$b = 3.94$ ft

9-38. 1.34 ft

9-40. 1.24 ft

9-42. 5.35 ft

9-44. 6.48 ft

9-46. 5.21 ft

9-48. (a) 2.08 ft
(b) 6.17 ft

9-50. 16.35 ft

9-52. $d = 2.22$ ft
$b = 4.44$ ft

9-54. (a) 4.12 ft
(b) $d = 1.44$ ft
$b = 2.88$ ft

9-56. $h = 1.104$ ft

9-58. $h = 1.29$ ft

CHAPTER 10

10-2. 43.8 sec

10-4. 1469 sec

10-6. 1066 sec

10-8. 3231 sec

10-10. 1757 sec

10-12. 0.705

10-14. 403 sec

CHAPTER 11

11-2. 9.52 lb →

11-4. 832 lb ⟋ 16.4 / 831.6

11-6. 67.62 lb →

11-8. 26.41 lb →

11-10. 27.43 lb →
47.51 lb ↑

11-12. (a) 9.22 lb
(b) 66.64 gpm

11-14. 171.3 fps

11-16. 89.6 percent

11-18. 98.81 fps

11-20. (a) 18.38 hp
(b) 47.05 psig

11-22. 2.46 hp

11-24. 728 lb
61.0 hp

11-26. 24.62 ft oil

11-28. 96.36 lb

11-30. 1283 lb

11-32. 18.55 ft oil

11-34. 156 lb

11-36. 717 lb

Index